60

D0389429

TRAILBLAZER OF AMERICAN SCIENCE

The Life of Joseph Henry

TRAILBLAZER of AMERICAN SCIENCE

The Life of Joseph Henry

by Sarah R. Riedman

Illustrated with photographs and diagrams

RAND McNALLY & COMPANY

CHICAGO · NEW YORK · SAN FRANCISCO

PRINTED IN U.S.A.
LIBRARY OF CONGRESS CATALOG
CARD NUMBER 61–6844
EDITION OF 1963 B

ACKNOWLEDGEMENTS

THE AUTHOR wishes to acknowledge her indebtedness to all those who, in one way or another, have generously helped to make this a better book: Paul H. Oehser, Chief of the Editorial and Publications Division of the Smithsonian Institution, Dr. Melba Phillips, of Washington University, St. Louis, Mo., and George F. Oslin, Publicity Director, The Western Union Telegraph Company, all three of whom have read the manuscript, making valuable suggestions and corrections (if any errors have been overlooked, they are the author's responsibility); Mr. John Franklin Jameson, Archivist, Smithsonian Institution, who was most helpful in furnishing the file of letters and documents and Mary Henry's diary, and who assisted in the selection of photographs; Alexander P. Clark, Curator of Manuscripts, and M. Halsey Thomas, Archivist, Princeton University, for their courteous assistance with source material in Princeton; Miss Juliet Wolohan, Senior Librarian, New York State Library, Albany, for her painstaking sifting of documents in the manuscript room.

Thanks go to the following persons and institutions for permission to reproduce the photographs: Smithsonian Institution for all pictures except those mentioned below; Princeton University Library (Joseph Henry Collection), for pictures on pages 48, 87, 108, 113, 127, 136, 207, and for the pictures on pages 121 and 124, not in the Joseph Henry Collection; New York State Library, for pictures on pages 25 and 32; Albany Academy for pictures on pages 59, 62, 73, 76, 78, 87, and 89, all from Bancroft Gherardi's address: "Joseph Henry's experiment in the Albany Academy, 1827-1832. Interpreted in the light of the present day (April 27, 1917)"; Albany Institute of History and Art for the picture of the Joseph Henry statue in Albany, on page 100; New York State History Museum, State Education Department, Albany, N.Y. for the picture of Henry's birthplace on page 19, and the Western Union Telegraph Company for pictures on pages 73, 174, and 176. Particular thanks go to Mrs. Mathilde Finch of the Princeton University Press for the photograph of Joseph Henry House (page 144) and for her hospitality in showing me through the house, now the home of Dean and Mrs. Jeremiah S. Finch. The diagrams on pages 47, 50, 53, 66, 96, and 133 were drawn especially for this book.

The Smithsonian Institution also furnished me with Smithsonian Miscellaneous Collections: *Memorial of Joseph Henry* (188), *Sketch of the Life and Contributions to Science of Professor Joseph Henry,* and Publication 4145, *The Smithsonian Institution.* These are recommended for those who wish to read more about Joseph Henry.

S.R.R.

February, 1961

CONTENTS

ILLUSTRATIONS

ILLUSTRATIONS

ILLUSTRATIONS

Campus Wire

College of New Jersey, Princeton. Noontime, any autumn in the late 1830s.

A visitor to the campus would be likely to witness a strange scene. We can reconstruct it from a few sparse records left by students and professors who delighted in this noontime ritual.

Some students are standing in small groups in front of Nassau Hall; others are hurrying down the campus paths to join them, caps in hand and books under arm. There is purpose in their brisk walk.

All eyes are turned expectantly toward Philosophical Hall, the three-story, gray building north of Nassau Hall.

"Will he be coming out soon?" a freshman asks.

"No, not until his students file out of that door," an upper classman answers, with the confidence of the initiate.

"What does the old professor look like? Long beard? Or is he bald?"

"The professor," his companion said impressively, "is quite the dapper young fellow. That's the amazing thing about this show."

"Where is the wire?" another freshman asks.

"Look, dunce, can't you see it strung through those trees? It reaches way across to his home on the other side of Nassau Hall."

"They say he wrapped the wire with silk from his wife's dress. But why—"

The question trails off, as the little crowd stiffens with excitement.

"There they come—the fellows in his class. Professor Henry will be along now."

The professor steps out of the door, and talk suddenly dies.

Tall and straight, the handsome young professor pauses in front of his laboratory building. His high forehead is unwrinkled, and his shock of brown hair reflects the glint of the sun. His green waistcoat and white cravat set off his clean-shaven face. Professor Henry has grown accustomed to his waiting audience, but he smiles at them as if this tribute were a delightful surprise.

"Gentlemen, I have ordered my lunch by signaling to Mrs. Henry through the electromagnetic telegraph in my laboratory. I have asked for slices of cold chicken, buttered bread, milk, and a cored apple," the professor announces.

Here and there a boy shifts from one leg to the other as the suspense mounts; all turn their heads in the direction of the professor's home across the campus.

After a few minutes of patient waiting, Sam, the professor's mulatto servant, opens the door of the Henry house, carrying Mr. Henry's lunch on a tray covered by a napkin. Mrs. Henry has decoded the message and sent him what he asked for.

The little group disperses, deeply impressed by having seen the "Campus Wire" demonstrated. "Campus Wire" is what the Princeton students called it, but it was the world's first telegraph line. Our story is about Joseph Henry, the man who constructed it.

Joseph Henry was a strangely neglected figure in his own day, but he is the hero of this story, which tells of the struggles, disappointments, and triumphs in a life devoted to science and the spread of knowledge. Joseph Henry's contributions have been many, not only to electromagnetism, but to every field of physics. More than a decade before the first commercial telegraphic message was sent, Professor Henry communicated with his wife across the campus. Then, as its first Secretary, he made the Smithsonian Institution famous throughout the world.

Today it stands as a great monument to the leading American scientist of the nineteenth century: Joseph Henry.

CHAPTER 1

Growing Up with the Country

JOSEPH HENRY's lively sense of the dramatic must have been stirred when he pictured the arrival of his grandparents in the New World. William Hendrie and Hugh Alexander, a farmer and a miller, had torn up their roots in Scotland and sailed with their families and a few scanty possessions to make a new life in this land of promise. Thousands of other families from the British Isles and Europe had taken the same tremendous leap into the unknown, but for each one the uprooting, the hopes and fears, were a fresh adventure.

Their arrival on American shores was excitement enough for any family, but there was a further, fateful twist in the drama. When the Hendries and the Alexanders left home, they knew in a vague way that the British king was having trouble with his rebellious American colonies. They sailed just about the time this trouble exploded in Lexington and Concord, but that news did not reach Britain until weeks later. Their little ship put down its anchor in New York Harbor on June 16, 1775. The next day the Battle of Bunker Hill started the war in earnest. Eight years of war, inflation, and profound upheavals lay ahead. Joseph's grandfathers, who had come to America in search of freedom, were soon to learn the price of winning and preserving it.

New York City was bewildering, and shocking too, in the eyes of these plain folk from Scotland. It was the most fashionable, frivolous—and also loyalist—of the colonial cities. Never had the newcomers seen such elegant brick houses, set in the garden green of June, such taverns overflowing with patrons, such carriages with coachmen and footmen in bright livery, or such people promenading the streets. Most of these people were dressed in the latest fashions from London and Paris, in silks and velvets and laces, in satin shoes with red heels, and with curled and powdered wigs. Nobody here was worried about the little disagreement between George III and his disobedient subjects up in the province of Massachusetts. The trouble was sure to blow over; meanwhile the New Yorkers amused themselves.

The Scottish immigrants arrived with their plans already shaped, probably with the advice of old friends who had come to America before them. Hugh Alexander, the miller, was bound for Delaware County above the Pennsylvania border. William Hendrie had been told of the rich farming lands on the Hudson River, and he was moving north.

This separation of the two families was a wrench. Joseph's grandparents had met on board the sailing vessel and the long, uncomfortable voyage had thrown the families into a close intimacy. As for the children, they acted like brothers and sisters. Young William Hendrie was especially fond of lovely little Ann Alexander who had the distinction, fascinating to all children, of being a twin. Her other half was named John. Another of her brothers, staggering under the name of Alexander Alexander (of course called Alec), was a special favorite.

Among the transformations apt to happen to strangers in a strange land, the Hendrie name soon evolved into "Henry," no doubt because people pronounced it carelessly. And by a quirk, the Henry family, arriving just a year before the newest and most daring form of government on earth was to be created, settled down in a locality in which the people held stubbornly to feudal traditions that belonged back in the Middle Ages. Joseph Henry's parents grew up in a strange double world, some of it rushing forward into the future, while the part immediately around them stagnated in the past.

The rich Hudson Valley, where the Henrys hoped to find free land for a farm, had a curious history. The Dutch claimed it because their explorer Henry Hudson had discovered it, and the Dutch West India Company founded the colony of New Netherland, which included the land along the river and at its mouth. When the British, who claimed all of America, began to settle the lands on both sides, the Company directors realized they must settle their empty colony in a hurry. And in their hurry they offered a bargain called patroonship. Any Dutch gentleman who would settle fifty colonists in New Netherland was given a great tract of land and absolute power over his colonists.

Each patroon was given sixteen miles of frontage on the Hudson River, with all the adjacent land he wished. Though Europe had long fought its way out of the feudal system, the Company revived a good deal of it to get the Hudson Valley settled. The patroon was overlord of his fifty families, with full political and military control over them; in any dispute he was also their magistrate. They could not leave his land for ten years, and a great part of their produce and their labor belonged to him by contract.

The Dutch settlers, more like serfs than sharecroppers, "owed" their patroon a share of their newborn stock, part of their crops as rent, and more of their crops plus labor because that was their hard bargain. When the British took over New Netherland this outmoded system remained, and the British, also in a hurry to colonize, bestowed huge land grants on their own fortune hunters, some of the estates running to a million acres. The rich Hudson Valley was thus the property of patroons and lords of the manor.

Even several decades after the Henrys arrived, the patroon, said a commentator of the day, could "swill his wine, loll on his cushions, fill his life with society, food and culture, and ride his fine saddle horse along the beautiful river valley and up to the backdrop of mountains."

Since the best lands belonged to the "best people," settlers with a strong pioneering spirit had to take the backlands where the soil was thin and grudging, and the only dependable crop was stones. It is not known which was the lot of William Henry—that of a vassal tenant on a patroonship, or of a poor homesteader wrestling with the stony soil near the Catskills. At any rate, the family settled in Albany County west of the river.

As for Hugh Alexander down in Delaware County, he built a mill with his bare hands, even to the shaping of the millstones, only to be driven out by Indians, who were fighting their own war for survival. By then the War of Independence was raging up and down New York State, and Alexander joined the Continental army as a soldier-mechanic. When the war was over, and his mill had been destroyed, he decided to move near the Hudson and develop the Salina salt mines. This showed his shrewdness, for the Revolution had been all but lost for want of salt, and now Britain had made it harder than ever to get smuggled supplies from islands near the Bahamas.

There was now a reunion between the Henry and Alexander families, who had been separated for nearly twenty years. The children who had played so happily together on the voyage from Scotland renewed their old affection. For our story the important result was the marriage of William Henry, the younger, and Ann Alexander, now a beautiful young woman.

They settled down in a small clapboard house on South Pearl Street in Albany. Their first son was named James and their second son was Joseph.

Though Mr. Hendrie spoke proudly of his Scottish ancestry, distantly related to the nobility of Argylshire, Joseph's parents had no reason to pretend that they were other than plain folk. William Henry's poor health did not permit him to gain his livelihood as farmer. As a sporadic day laborer, Mr. Henry occupied a lower rung in the social ladder than some of his country neighbors who, though no less poor, proudly called themselves freeholders because they had escaped from the patroon system.

Ann Alexander, Joseph's mother, retained her gentle beauty, despite hardships and poverty, and was respected for her fine mind and strong character. To her fell the lot of bringing up her family in addition to nursing a sick husband who was frequently out of work. Much of her strength of character she drew from her deeply religious spirit, but mingled with her stern Calvinism was a warm understanding love which enveloped her family.

When Joseph was born, the event was recorded in the family Bible as December 9, 1797, and was so transferred to the baptismal register of the First Presbyterian Church in Albany. However the mistake may have occurred, the date was not corrected—to December 17, 1799—until Joseph Henry reached manhood. His cousin Stephen Alexander, who was Joseph's age, was sure that the year was 1799; Joseph's daughter remembered him counting his age from the turn of the century, and the record on his modest insurance policy finally clinched his year of birth as 1799.

Joseph's father left little to remember him by, except that

Joseph Henry's birthplace, identified in 1899 by his niece, Agnes Henry. The man is "Old Jack," a Scot "chore man"

he was sickly. From his mother, Joseph inherited his slender figure, well-cut features, and fine complexion. And he could hardly fail to show the effect of her strict character molding. In a Presbyterian home this meant learning to respect the moral virtues and obeying a high standard of ethical principles. Early in life Joseph clearly knew right from wrong, thanks to his mother. At the same time he was full of boyish liveliness and imagination which made him popular with his friends, but called forth gentle reproofs from his elders.

When Joseph was only seven, Ann Henry sent him to live with her twin brother John, who lived with Grandmother Alexander on a farm in Galway. Perhaps Joseph meant one mouth too many to feed in the straitened Henry house, perhaps she knew he would thrive better with the Alexanders, who were prospering as the Henrys went down in the world. As distances were measured in those days, the village of Galway was far away—about 35 miles northwest of Albany. Measured in human feelings, it meant that Joseph hardly saw his mother for the next seven years. Joseph often related years later that when he was finally reunited with his mother he thought that his home had been on the opposite side of the street. He said this prank, played by his childish memory, divided his life into two periods: the part when he lived on one side of the street, and the part when he lived on the other.

Joseph's uncle John did what he could to look after the boy, sending him to the village school where Israel Phelps, a run-of-the-mill teacher, saw nothing special in the boy. Nor did Joseph distinguish himself as a pupil. For him, going to school was an accepted chore like dressing in the morning or bringing in the firewood.

By dint of dull repetition, under the uninspiring Phelps, Joseph learned to read, write, and "do sums." Like all boys on a farm he was expected to do chores which he didn't always remember, to the annoyance of his grandmother.

What older people called idleness and day-dreaming was just Joseph's way of getting lost in imaginative thought. And as he later recalled, lost he was—behind the barn or in an open field, lying in the quiet seclusion of tall grass. What if his grandmother called to him because he had forgotten to wash the milk pails? Joseph was far away gazing at the clouds and thinking thoughts that had nothing to do with the demands of grown-ups.

What made clouds take such fantastic shapes? What made the blue of the sky? Where did the stars go in the daytime? Neither Mr. Phelps nor anyone else he knew could or would think of answering such questions.

He was ten years old when his uncle arranged for the boy's first job, as part-time helper in Mr. Broderick's general store. Mr. Broderick was a kindly man and took a liking to the little lad. A bright boy was a great help in a village store.

Joseph had no complaints about his duties. He had to sweep the store, keep the fire going, and dust the counters. Some things about store-keeping he liked. He would run up the ladder to get some special ware from the top shelves, or roll paper into a horn to wrap a few sticks of cinnamon or peppermint candy. He would politely carry out the purchases to the carriage of a well-to-do shopper, or go to the storeroom back of the shop for fresh supplies of sugar or calico.

The general store was also the village post office, a place for getting news or spreading gossip, a station for the stagecoach, a haven in rainstorms or blizzards, and the social center of Galway. The local workers played a game of checkers on a board painted on the stump of a big tree, or argued about the possibility of President James Madison's declaring war with England. A friendly boy could find much to interest him in the center of village life, and Joseph enjoyed the grown-up talk that went on around him.

Mr. Broderick had respect for learning, even if he had little of it himself. He saw to it that Joseph continued to attend the village school, releasing him from his store duties in the afternoons. There was still time to spare for games with the boys and even for solitary dreaming. He had not yet discovered the possibility of reading books for pleasure. That happened quite by accident.

Among the few things Joseph could consider his very own was a pet rabbit. One day the rabbit escaped from his hutch, scurrying off into a field with Joseph in hot pursuit. As the animal sought refuge under the village church, Joseph followed him, crawling beneath the floor. Through the half-darkness around the foundation he saw chinks of light overhead, and with a little probing found a few loose boards that he easily dislodged. A little squirming and he could squeeze up through an opening in the floor. There he was in a small room, a part of the church he had never seen—the village library.

The magic of finding what was to him a secret place was exciting enough, but here were shelves of books! He reached out for one that attracted him, feeling that he was plucking forbidden fruit. It seemed so different from the dog-eared reader Mr. Phelps offered in school. As he later said, it was the first book he had ever opened voluntarily.

The book he chanced to pick up was *The Fool of Quality* by Sir Philip Brooke. Forgetting the rabbit chase, he remained to read it for as long as he could stay away without being missed. Then he left the same way he entered. For days afterwards he returned through the secret passage until he finished the story.

Why was Joseph fascinated with this book? It was the story of two sons of an English nobleman. The older, heir to his father's title and wealth, had every opportunity of education, but he turned out to be lazy, shiftless, and spoiled, while the younger, placed as a foster child with a farmer's wife, developed habits of industry and sterling qualities. Making the hero his mouthpiece, the author spoke his mind for reform and against oppression of the poor. Poverty, he said, came from ignorance, not laziness or lack of ability. Progress came from honest labor, construction of roads and canals, productive farming methods, and development of industry. The neglected younger son, the Fool of Quality, left to his own resources as a simple farm boy, became the spokesman for progress.

Some of Brooke's views on poverty and oppression, law and religion were vaguely familiar. Joseph had heard similar talk from the village folk who gathered in Mr. Broderick's store, for resentment against the remnants of the evil patroon system was strong. Perhaps Joseph saw some resemblance to himself in the farm-boy hero, but whatever the attraction of this, his first book, it opened a new world for him. His interest in reading impelled him day after day to steal into the library through his secret entrance. After a while the secret was out, and it was Mr. Broderick who discovered it.

This was lucky for Joseph. His kind employer recognized his hunger to learn, and got him permission to use the reading room without crawling through a hole in the floor. From then on they both read the books and discussed them.

Joseph's discovery of the riches to be found in books had another happy consequence. Not everyone had the privilege of visiting the library. Sharpening his memory, and filling in with his imagination, Joseph related what he read to friends. They listened with wonder to the stories, for Joseph had unexpected gifts in telling them. About this time he went home on a rare visit and was taken to a stage play in Albany. On his return to Galway he acted it out, scene by scene, taking the part of each player in turn.

During his stay at Galway, Joseph's father died. The death of Uncle John soon after was perhaps an even greater loss, because he had become more of a father to Joseph than his own ailing parent, and it meant that his pleasant years in Galway were over. Joseph, now fourteen, was needed at home to help support the family. He returned to Albany, where his mother had already made arrangements for his future.

At first glance a visitor would have considered the Albany of 1814 a most pleasant, lively, and prosperous town. It had the air of a capital city; it boasted of fine eating places, theaters, and fashionable shops; well-dressed urbane people walked its streets. But there was another Albany not immediately apparent to an outsider. At the river's edge, in the southern end of town, known as the Pasture, was the poor section where the workers lived in crowded, ramshackle dwellings. Here Ann Henry earned her living by renting rooms to boarders.

In many ways Albany was unlike any other city of post-Revolutionary times. It was the center of Rensselaerwyck, a semifeudal empire that took in all of Albany, Rensselaer, and part of Columbia Counties. Its overlord was Stephen Van Rensselaer III who gloried in his nickname of Good Patroon. He was by far the richest and most influential of the Hudson Valley society folk who bore British or French Huguenot names—Livingston, Morris, and Jay—or Dutch—Hardenburgh, Van Cortland, Schuyler, and Van Rensselaer.

The Rensselaer family had for more than two hundred years been the owners of the largest estate in the region. In spite of the Revolutionary War they still retained their baronial power. The Good Patroon, Congressman, and one-time general was the acknowledged leader of the landed aristocracy, and

Stephen
Van Rensselaer

the political power behind the legislature. During his patroonship, he had a strong influence in the framing of most of the laws passed by the New York Legislature. In 1805 he was responsible for enactment of state laws permitting the imposition of rents as a condition of buying land. No one could buy a parcel outright, without pledging to the landlord a perpetual share of his produce.

Because he was charitable, contributed to hospitals, helped to build and maintain churches, supported agricultural research to increase the productivity of his farms, Rensselaer was called the Good Patroon. But his tenants were impoverished by heavy taxes and annual contributions to the patroon of "ten to fourteen bushels of wheat, four fat fowls," and by their labor, with team and wagon thrown in for building roads.

The Van Rensselaer manor house stood at the north end of the city. This impressive mansion, with its elegant drawing rooms where the flower of Albany society gathered, was a symbol of decaying feudal power.

In the center of town were the public buildings, shops, and taverns. Along the river stood small factories for making cloth, guns, clocks, mirrors, finery, and jewelry. Since rivers were still the principal highways for shipping, Albany offered a measure of prosperity to small factory owners, shopkeepers, and artisans whose goods were sold mainly to the wealthy.

The rest of the people were attached to farms, worked in the factories, or took day jobs constructing turnpikes along which the younger people were beginning to move west in search of greener fields.

The class lines in Albany were sharply drawn, despite the fact that the young nation had declared its faith in democracy and free enterprise. A veteran of the Revolution might be refused a seat in the Albany-Troy stage because he was shabbily dressed. Newspaper editors snobbishly remarked in their columns that cigar smoking had lost its charm for society folk because every dirty little shop boy had taken it up.

Where in this pattern of Albany society did Joseph Henry fit? In the years he spent on his uncle's farm he had developed no inclination to become a farmer. His father left him no money with which to open a factory or a shop. He could hardly dream of taking up a profession, which meant money for study. Besides, Joseph had not shown any aptitude in that direction. His mother, facing the facts, decided he would have to learn a trade.

Soon after he came back to Albany, he was apprenticed to a watchmaker and silversmith, Mr. John F. Doty. It is highly likely that Mrs. Henry considered a jeweler's trade a cut above others. His brother James had gone to work in a bookshop, also a rather genteel way to make a living.

The jeweler's trade demanded some skill in using fine tools, and the work, if exacting, was not back-breaking. Besides, only the upper classes could order fine silver or a delicate watch. Joseph would be thrown in with more privileged people than his neighbors in the Pasture.

Nothing in Joseph's later life indicated that he looked forward to the prospect of becoming a skilled jeweler. In fact, it must have been confining to a boy who liked people, activity, lively talk, and the comings and goings he had enjoyed in Mr. Broderick's store.

Whatever Joseph's own plans may have been for his future, circumstances were against his becoming a silversmith. It was not a moment in which a luxury trade could flourish. Times were bad. The country was still suffering from the effects of the Embargo Act of 1807 on foreign trade. In the war between France and England, President Jefferson had tried to keep the United States free from entanglement. He had urged Congress to keep American goods, ships, and sailors at home to avoid getting pulled into a foreign war. The stoppage of American trade with foreign ports brought the wartime prosperity to a sudden end. Exports dropped, merchants and shippers went bankrupt, laborers lost their jobs, and hard times spread, especially in the cities of the North. Then on top of this, the War of 1812 and its aftermath nearly bankrupted the country.

Despite his struggle to stay in business, Mr. Doty was forced to give up his shop after Joseph had been training with him for two years. Mr. Doty said he would not have made a silversmith anyway, because he was too "dull." Whether his master said this to console Joseph for the loss of his apprenticeship, or because he suspected that the boy had other interests, it is clear that he knew the boy's heart wasn't in his craft.

As things turned out, this wasn't a complete loss of two precious years, because Henry later proved his skill in building apparatus, and displayed rather a knack for handling fine tools.

While still apprenticed to Mr. Doty, Joseph developed an absorbing interest in the theater. From the time he saw his first play as a child, everything about the stage drew him like a magnet. Albany was more advanced in certain respects than most other American cities, and boasted a sophisticated legitimate theater.

It was managed by John Bernard, a distinguished English comedian, who gathered a stock company of professional actors, some of whom made a name for themselves on the stage.

Henry spent many of his spare evenings in Mr. Bernard's theater, a diversion which must have distressed his Presbyterian mother. Play-acting was not yet accepted as a respectable sort of entertainment by people of her deep piety. It was perhaps proper for the carriage crowd, but not meant for the poor. Besides, the price of admission was beyond the means of an apprentice with a widowed mother.

If Joseph found a way to see every play on the boards, it must have been because he made friends with the stagehands and was permitted to see the play free from the wings. Probably he made himself useful with props and shifting scenery and thus entered the world of the theater as a stagehand. Joseph's interest was not merely that of a passive playgoer; he dreamed of making the stage his career.

He chanced upon an amateur group—*The Rostrum*—that

offered the opportunity he was looking for. At the end of the day's work at the jewelry shop he was off to the dramatic club, where he took acting parts, helped with staging, and even wrote plays. He wrote a comedy and a dramatization of his favorite novel, both of which were produced by the club. At sixteen he was elected president of *The Rostrum.* Joseph was well on the way toward fulfilling his life ambition—or at least so he thought—when something happened to change his course.

An accidental injury to his leg forced him into confinement at home. To occupy himself during his illness he picked up a book lent him by Robert Boyle (not the chemist, of course), a recent arrival from Scotland, who was boarding in the house. The book by Gregory, an English clergyman, published in London in 1808, bore the formidable title: *Lectures on Experimental Philosophy, Astronomy and Chemistry.*

Here was a book that lured the curious reader with such provocative questions as:

"You throw a stone or shoot an arrow into the air; why does it not go forward in a line with the direction you give it? . . . On the contrary, why does flame or smoke always mount upward, although no force is used to set them in that direction?"

Joseph was enthralled. This book was different from romances, novels, and plays, as different as the *Fool of Quality* was from a speller! It was his introduction to the realm of science, a way of answering questions about the world of things, of explaining familiar phenomena of life. It set his imagination afire as no other book had done. In the evenings when Mr. Boyle had finished his supper, the two would pore over its pages, and talk about the wonders it contained long after the candle flame had flickered out. Mr. Boyle, recognizing

Joseph's enthusiasm, gladly parted with the book, which became one of Joseph's treasured possessions.

Years later, he wrote on its flyleaf:

> This book, by no means a profound work, has under Providence exerted a remarkable influence upon my mind. It accidentally fell into my hands when I was about sixteen years old, and was the first book I ever read with attention. It opened to me a new world of thought and enjoyment; it fixed my attention upon the study of nature, and caused me to resolve at the time of reading it that I would immediately devote myself to the acquisition of knowledge.

Joseph always had a sense of the dramatic. He saw this encounter with Mr. Gregory's book as a turning point in his life, despite the ardor with which he had previously determined to be an actor and writer. As soon as he was well enough to leave the house, he went to *The Rostrum*, and in a formal valedictory address to its members forever put that part of his life behind him. . . .

CHAPTER 2

The Making of a Scientist

IN LATER YEARS people who knew Henry well, knew his virtues and his foibles, his strengths and weaknesses, sometimes pointed to a streak of indecision in his character. Politicians accused him of straddling, and friends regretted that his difficulty in making up his mind sometimes prevented a prompt decision in important matters. When this failing was mentioned, Henry admitted it was a lifelong habit, and recalled this story from his childhood.

While he was still in Galway he went to the shoemaker to order a pair of shoes. "What will you have, round or square toes?" the cobbler asked. Joseph couldn't make up his mind. Unable to settle this simple question, he asked the shoemaker to start work, promising to return and tell him what he wanted.

Joseph came every day to watch the progress of his shoes, but always left without deciding the shape of the toes. One day when he returned for his usual inspection, he was surprised to find his shoes finished. The shoemaker had settled the problem in his own way—he presented the boy with one square-toed and one round-toed boot.

In the small matter of footwear, Henry had wavered, and

was punished for it by having to wear out his very odd shoes. But once he renounced acting as a career, there was no indecision as to the path he was to follow.

He was now determined to explore nature through scientific study. But first he had a great deal to learn that other youths of sixteen who had chosen the path of learning already knew. Not that he couldn't match wits with many boys who had more formal schooling, but he knew that he was woefully unprepared for prying into the secrets of nature. Much of what he needed to know was not taught in the schools of his time, but Joseph had a full measure of eagerness and grit, and could teach himself. For the rest he would get what he could by attending classes.

At once he registered for night classes in the Albany Academy. In the three or four years of the school's existence it had earned a reputation for good teachers and earnest students. In fact the president of Union College called it "a

Albany Boys Academy

college in disguise." Joseph enrolled for evening courses in geometry and mechanics, and in the daytime took lessons from an itinerant teacher in English grammar. Before long he had acquired enough skill in parsing, syntax, word derivation, verse, meter, and phonetics to teach others.

To earn his tuition in the Academy he became an itinerant himself, traveling to homes on the outskirts of town, offering lessons in grammar. In the meantime he looked about for something better, and found that one of the district schools had an opening. The school authorities would have preferred someone older for the job, but since Joseph was willing to accept a salary of eight dollars a month, he got the appointment. Within one month he proved himself as a teacher, and his salary was raised to fifteen dollars.

What with teaching, attending classes at the Academy, and preparing his lessons for both, Joseph worked sixteen hours a day. But he stood up well under this schedule. Strong in body and buoyant in spirit, he never felt tired. At the end of seven months he passed his Academy examinations with honors, and was ready to begin the study of calculus.

Dr. T. Romeyn Beck, the Academy principal, had a rather unusual education for a headmaster. A graduate of Union College in Schenectady and of the College of Physicians and Surgeons of New York, he had prepared himself for medicine. Having studied under Dr. David Hosack, a famous physician and botanist, Dr. Beck became interested in natural science. For several years he practiced medicine in Albany, but readily exchanged what he considered a dreary practitioner's life for the principalship of the Academy. Under his leadership the school flourished.

Dr. Beck at once recognized in Joseph a young man of unusual determination and scholastic ability. It wasn't often that students applied themselves with such earnestness to their studies. He wanted very much to keep the youth in school, and when an opportunity arose for a less time-consuming job than district school teaching, he was happy to recommend Joseph for it.

General Stephen Van Rensselaer, who headed the board of trustees of the Academy, needed a private tutor for his children. He asked Dr. Beck to suggest one of his best students, and Dr. Beck chose Joseph, who could not himself have picked a better post.

His teaching duties were far from onerous. Three hours a day were all that was required of him, and teaching the wealthy little fellows was easier than drilling a class in the 3 Rs. Perhaps the one-time apprentice saw the irony of his situation—teaching the sons of the Good Patroon manners and deportment after the model created by Samuel Richardson in his novel, *Sir Charles Grandison*. But Joseph discharged his duties well, and made little gentlemen of the patroon heirs.

Best of all, his light duties gave him time for his own studies. Like many students of his day he was self-taught. There were no facilities to help him—no distinguished teachers, properly equipped laboratories, textbooks, or even well-stocked libraries. He had to rely on his own efforts for both his education and his livelihood.

There was the nub of the problem. What studies would prepare him for earning a living? Patient and understanding as Mrs. Henry was, she was wearing herself to the bone to maintain the household for her two sons and her little daughter Nancy. What profession would Joseph's learning lead him to? The choices were narrow: one went to college to train either for the ministry or the law. But science was not yet a profession; it was considered a hobby only a gentleman could afford, a leisure-time occupation for an amateur. A poor young man could hardly aspire to a professor's career at Harvard, the College of New Jersey (later Princeton) or Pennsylvania—"Ivy League" schools even then.

The only profession in which Henry could hope to develop his interest in science was medicine, and so he made his decision. He would take up the study of "physick." The Academy offered both anatomy and physiology, the beginner's courses in medicine. This was at least a start toward a profession. Dr. Beck, always eager to help this exceptional boy, invited him to assist in his chemical demonstrations.

Scientific lectures in those days were more of an intellectual pastime than a classroom procedure. To be sure, a handful of serious students attended them, but most of the audience were fashionable visitors who came for the amusement and stimulation of the demonstrations that usually accompanied the chemical lectures. The professor was expected to put on a sort of show of experiments. As Dr. Beck's assistant, Henry not only prepared the apparatus, but contributed to the novelty of the experiments.

Judging from an account given by a student of the Academy in the early 1820s it was a "pleasure and privilege" to watch some experiment on steam or with a small steam engine. One of the experimenters was "Joseph Henry, as yet unknown to fame, but already giving promise of those rare qualities of mind and character which have since raised him to the very first rank among experimental philosophers of his time." Thus, Dr. Beck's chemical assistant made the most of the opportunity of "prosecuting his investigations in chemistry, electricity, and galvanism."

Along with his studies and scientific demonstrations, young Henry continued with tutoring. After two years with the Rensselaer children, he became private tutor to Henry James, who was to become the father of William James the psychologist, and Henry James the novelist. Henry James had lost a leg through an accident at play, and could not attend school. Joseph Henry prepared him for college.

Joseph now made another friend at the Academy who advanced his knowledge in the sciences. Like Dr. Beck, Amos Eaton had not trained for teaching. He graduated with a degree in law from Williams College and in 1802 settled in Catskill as a lawyer and real estate agent. By coincidence he too came under the influence of the physician-botanist Dr. Hosack. While carrying on his law business, Eaton gave popular lectures in botany and wrote a manual on the subject that went through eight editions. In 1815 he took scientific courses under Professors Silliman and Ives at Yale. A diligent student, he was invited to give lectures in geology and botany at Amherst, Northampton, and Middlebury.

Amos Eaton had a knack for making friends of influential people. In 1818, Governor De Witt Clinton asked him to deliver a lecture before the New York State Legislature, which eventually resulted in the establishment of a state geological survey. In 1820, under the patronage of Stephen Van Rensselaer, he made a geological and agricultural survey of Albany and Rensselaer Counties and later helped the patroon survey the district around the Erie Canal.

Amos Eaton was a competent chemist, as well as a geologist and botanist. He was the first to establish in America the method of teaching chemistry through laboratory experiments by the students, replacing the demonstrations by the professor. Very likely Henry attended his course in botany to acquaint himself with plants and herbs from which doctors prepared their own medicines. Eaton, like Beck, recognized Henry's talents, and later, when the Rensselaer School was opened in Troy, in 1826, he recommended him for an appointment as an examiner in mathematics.

Another unpaid job which Henry had during this period was that of Librarian of the Institute of Arts and Sciences. The Institute, a society to promote the useful arts and the spread of scientific knowledge, had about two hundred members, with Rensselaer as president. Henry had charge of the library of three hundred books to which he himself contributed not only books but geological specimens and a container of marsh gas. This gas, that burns with a beautiful clear light, is found in mines. Henry had probably collected it on some geological excursion with Amos Eaton.

Despite his remarkable progress after only a few years of digging for knowledge, Henry was modest about his attainments. It would hardly have entered his head to put on a scientific show of his own. But he was persuaded by his sponsors to demonstrate his experiments with steam before the members of the Institute. He was twenty-five years old when he read his first paper: "On the Chemical and Mechanical Effects of Steam; with experiments designed to illustrate the great reduction of temperature in steam of high elasticity when suddenly expanded."

People were just beginning to learn about the uses of steam in industry, and a lecture on the subject excited the interest that a popular lecture on the uses of atomic energy does today. On August 17, 1807, Robert Fulton's *Clermont* had steamed up the Hudson, making the trip from New York to Albany in thirty-two hours, but on October 30, 1824 when Henry delivered his lecture, the idea of "steam wagons" for transportation on land was still in the talking stage.

The essence of Henry's lecture was that the temperature of escaping steam from a boiler went down as the temperature and pressure inside the boiler increased. He demonstrated this by holding a thermometer in jets of steam that were permitted to escape from the boiler as heat continued to be applied to it.

To clinch the point of the experiment, he placed his hand over the jet of escaping steam to show that it was not hot enough to scald. Actually, Henry discovered nothing original by this experiment, but to an audience uninitiated in science this was a most impressive spectacle. That they didn't fully understand it only added to the mystery.

The first demonstration a success, he was invited to read a second paper: "The Production of Cold by the Rarefaction of Air." From the *Transactions* of the Albany Institute we get a detailed description of the demonstration.

Half a pint of water was poured into a five-gallon spherical copper vessel. A tube, one-quarter of an inch in diameter with a number of perforations at the lower end and a stopper at the other, was screwed into the neck of the vessel. Only the lower end dipped into the water, and a number of the holes were above the surface of the water. Using a powerful condensing pump, he introduced air into the vessel to a pressure of nine atmospheres. During the condensation the vessel became warm.

Henry waited until the apparatus cooled down to room temperature and then opened the stopcock. The air rushed out with great violence, carrying with it some of the water, which instantly turned to snow. After a few seconds the tube became filled with ice, which almost completely blocked the exit of the air. He then unscrewed the neck of the vessel to allow the condensed air to escape around the sides of the screw. The suddenly expanded air lowered the temperature of the interior of the vessel, causing the remainder of the water to freeze.

In a room in which the temperature was 80° Fahrenheit, water froze! The audience gasped at the spectacular proof of the fact that when air is allowed to expand suddenly the temperature drops considerably—in this case, enough to cause water to freeze.

For the elite of Albany this was a remarkable curiosity, and the experimenter who performed the feat a clever showman. It was a whole generation later when the principle Henry illustrated was put to use in commercial ice-making.

The period during which Henry was immersed in study and self-improvement was one of great movement westward. Conestoga wagons, farm horses, and ponies carried families toward the Ohio country, with its promise of rich valley lands and profitable trade with the Indians. Movement of men and goods meant the building of roads and turnpikes, especially to and from waterways. But haulage over land was expensive, by whatever means. Wherever possible goods were carried by water, on rivers and lakes.

Then came the era of canal building. The greatest of the engineering projects of the day was the construction of the Erie Canal, connecting the Hudson River at Albany with Lake Erie at Buffalo. In 1817, the New York State Legislature, urged by Governor De Witt Clinton, authorized its construction. Rensselaer, as the State Commissioner, with the help of Amos Eaton, made the first survey for the 363-mile water link that was completed by 1825.

The canal, popularly called "Clinton's Ditch," became the great water route to the West. It reduced the freight-carrying time from New York to Buffalo from twenty to six days, and the cost of shipping grain from the West by four-fifths. New York became the largest shipping center in the United States.

Though Henry had no part in these developments, he was now and then caught up in the mainstream of swift-moving events. A new road was projected between West Point and Lake Erie, and quite unexpectedly Henry was offered the job of surveying it.

What did he know of surveying? Ought he to take on work that would interrupt his studies? Still, the offer was tempting. Although his sinewy frame, strong constitution, and six-foot height hardly betrayed it, his health was beginning to show the effects of confinement in the laboratory and his long hours of study. Working out of doors offered a welcome change. Besides, the pay was good. As it turned out, this was the only job he was ever to have on which he could save a modest sum. He accepted the offer.

The work was hard and the terrain rugged. In winter it meant trudging through deep snow every foot of the way through unfamiliar country, but he stuck to the task. No one could ever say that Henry flinched from any job he undertook, and he applied himself to this one with his usual earnestness. In fact, he came to like the work of following the line to its completion. So well done was the job that he was recommended for a position with the U.S. Corps of Civil Engineers. Another offer, to supervise the construction of a canal in Ohio followed, and still another to manage a mine in Mexico.

Just when Henry was weighing these opportunities, Dr. Beck called to tell him of a vacancy in the Albany Academy. He had only to say "yes" and there was an appointment waiting for him as Professor of Mathematics and Natural Philosophy, as Physics was then called.

Once again Henry was forced to make an important decision. Ambitious and able men sought their futures in the developing industries, in railroads and commerce. Peter Cooper was envisioning a wheeled steam engine to run on rails. He was working on his *Tom Thumb,* the first railway locomotive. There were many opportunities offered in the development of the country's harbors and the improvement of its waterways. This was the era when young men of Henry's ability took leading places in the development of an expanding country.

Had Henry longed for wealth he could easily have turned his back on struggle and poverty, which had been his lot from early childhood. His surveying job paid him nearly $2,100, twice what he would get as a professor years later. Having succeeded in this work, he had paved the way for still more profitable jobs had he wished to take up the offers.

No doubt Henry had some help in arriving at his decision.

Room on second floor of Albany Academy, originally occupied by Joseph Henry

The men whom he looked up to most in these early years were his mentors, Dr. Beck and Professor Eaton. Eaton had by this time earned a reputation as an innovator in education and was senior professor in the Rensselaer School of Science, later to become the Rensselaer Polytechnic Institute. Dr. Beck was still the honored principal of the Academy.

We can imagine them urging their promising student and budding teacher:

"Henry, anyone can be a surveyor or engineer, but only a few have your talents as an experimenter."

Perhaps Henry's modesty would have made him protest:

"But I still have so much to learn; how can I hope to teach others?"

"You are a born teacher. Your duty lies here, where you can inspire the youth of our nation," would have been a likely reply.

His sponsors knew that an appeal to "duty" would strike the right chord in Henry's heart, for no young man had a greater sense of responsibility. And so he agreed, in the spring of 1826, to take his post as professor in the fall of that year. In taking this step he set aside his former resolve to become a doctor, and gave up offers of wealth and comfort in industry. With the same finality with which he had broken off a career in the theater ten years earlier, Henry now embarked on the life of a scholar.

Having made his decision to enter academic life, Henry lost no time in preparing himself for his lectures and in devising experiments. This represented an innovation in early nineteenth-century teaching of science. Without a doubt, he endeavored to learn the newer methods introduced by his former teacher Eaton, now recognized as an enlightened educator, not satisfied with reading from a textbook.

Along with Eaton he also undertook a project to make a geographical and geological survey of the counties neighboring on Albany. He prepared tables showing the mileages of the various local routes, and the elevations at different points.

He also initiated during this time some simple meteorological work under a system established by the Regents of the University of the State of New York. Each academy chartered by the state was supplied with a thermometer and a rain-gauge, and was required to keep a daily register of the temperature, rainfall, and wind direction. These figures were compiled annually and reported to the Regents.

Starting these observations in 1826, Henry continued to keep records for several years. In the report filed in 1830, he included also an accurate tabulation of the latitude, longitude, and elevations of some forty meteorological stations, in which he attempted to show some relationship of weather phenomena to physical geography.

Primitive as his observations were, they were the beginnings of his interest in weather phenomena and showed his life-long eagerness to enlarge his knowledge of the world of nature.

CHAPTER 3

Electricity and Magnetism

WITH THE ACCEPTANCE of the post on the staff of the Academy, Henry must have considered himself at the pinnacle of his career. If his mother had any part in his decision, or if she was happy for him is not known. The record is a complete blank on this point. It is known, however, that another member of the family took pride in his achievement. Alexander S. Alexander, a relative in Schenectady wrote:

> I write to tell you I have seen an extract from your inaugural address and the only reason I was not more delighted was that I could not see the whole of the production which is worthy of the Professor, a feast to the *man* of intellect as well as to the *man* of taste. From what I could gather from the *Argus* I must congratulate you on its success at the time of its delivery before a learned and polite auditory. May your professorship be as splendid as its commencement was brilliant. . . .

Neither Henry nor his family dreamed that the professorship was only the beginning of a poor boy's rise to international fame.

Henry was one of four professors in a school of one hundred

and fifty students. By modern standards for a professor of mathematics, Henry's knowledge of the subject was far from remarkable, and "natural philosophy" included the broad range of subjects that today would be covered in courses in physics, chemistry, geology, meteorology, mechanics, and perhaps even principles of engineering. What he may have lacked in depth of knowledge he more than made up in the broad scope of the subjects, and in skill of presentation, and he displayed enough of both to leave a lasting impression on his students.

One of them, Orlando Meads, recalled years later that the Academy "was not unworthy of the high qualifications he brought to it; for in that day few of the colleges of this country afforded such a large and thorough course of instruction . . . [and] his lectures excited great interest and admiration. He had rare power as a lecturer. With always a full knowledge of his subject, his language was well chosen and exact, his elocution dignified and impressive, and he had in a rare degree . . . the faculty characteristic of the highest order of minds—of presenting the deepest truths with a clearness and simplicity that brought them within the grasp of ordinary minds."

Just as Joseph Henry's experience as a silversmith's apprentice stood him in good stead with the construction of apparatus, his theatrical experience came in handy in dramatizing his lectures. From Eaton he learned the value of illustrating them with experiments, but what he added was his boyish enthusiasm, reflected in his sparkling eyes and in every quick and supple movement of his body. While lecturing, the professor took on all the magnetism of the showman, gathering his audience around him with a telling gesture of the hand and a sense of mystery in his voice.

When Joseph Henry began his studies, not a great deal

was known about electricity and magnetism, though even in ancient times some isolated and sporadic discoveries had been made. Thales, the Greek philosopher, was the first to record that when amber was rubbed with fur, it picked up bits of dried leaves, feathers, or hair.

Many centuries rolled by before Sir William Gilbert, interested mainly in magnetism of the loadstone, also studied friction with amber. He decided that magnetism and electricity were two different forces. Many a time he amused and fascinated Queen Elizabeth with his tricks of rubbing sulphur, jet, resin, wax, and glass with silk or flannel, making them attract light objects. This was electricity, and Sir William was the first to use the word, which he took from the Greek word *electron,* meaning amber.

Any school boy or girl today would recognize that this was static electricity. When you comb your hair with a hard rubber comb on a day when the air is dry the hair crackles, its loose ends are attracted by the comb, and if you do this in a darkened room in front of a mirror you can see tiny sparks jump from the comb to the hair. But in the court of the Queen it was all a mystery.

Then about the middle of the seventeenth century, Otto von Guericke, mayor of Magdeburg, Germany, made the first machine that generated static electricity. Instead of rubbing resin with fur by hand, he set up a ball of sulphur on a shaft and rotated it by turning a handle. A piece of silk or wool was wrapped tightly around the sulphur ball, and as it revolved, friction between the two caused heavy charges of electricity to accumulate on the surface of the sulphur. The longer and faster the ball was spun the greater the electrical charge that was generated. He also discovered that electrified objects, touching non-electrified ones, transferred some of their

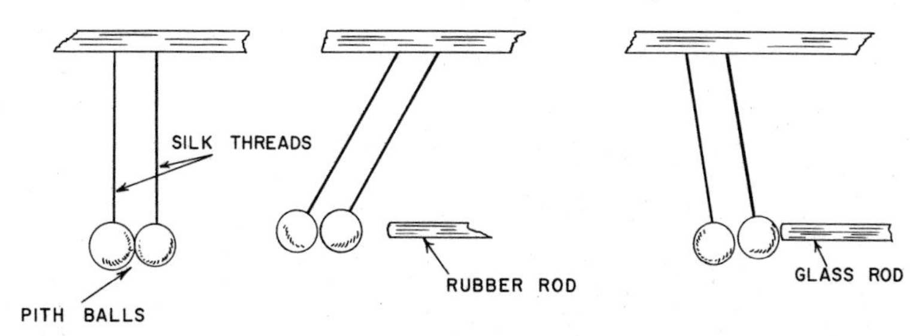

The positively charged glass rod attracts the pith ball; the negatively charged rubber rod repels it

electricity. That is what happens when you get a shock from touching the hand of someone who has shuffled across a thick carpet.

Another century went by before the Frenchman, C.F. de C. du Fay, showed that the charges produced by rubbing a glass rod and that of a stick of resin were not alike. He called one "vitreous" and the other "resinous," thinking that these were two different kinds of electricity. In this he was wrong, but he did correctly find that *like* charges repel each other, while *unlike* ones attract each other. As he put it, "the two electricities repel themselves but attract each other."

Then Benjamin Franklin suggested that the charge on a glass rod stroked with fur be called *positive,* while that on a rubber rod stroked with silk would be *negative.* But as he stated, positive or negative, there was only one kind of electricity. Actually, neither is produced alone, but his terms are still the ones we use today for opposite charges. The fur used to rub the rubber rod becomes positive, repelling other positively charged particles, and the silk used with the glass rod acquires a negative charge, repelling a negatively charged object. When electricity is produced by contact between two un-

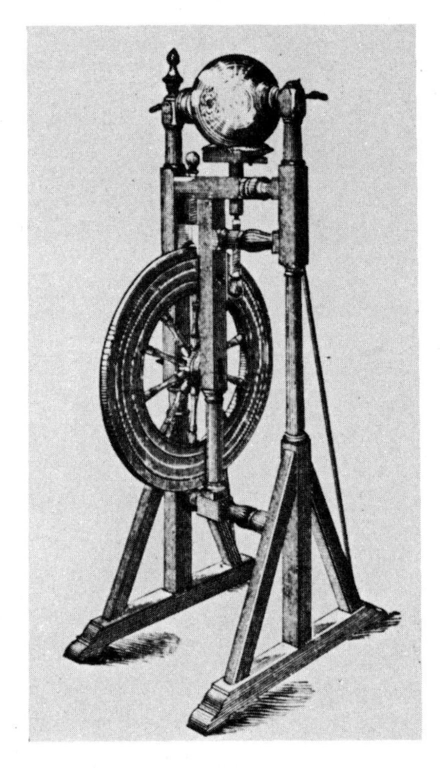

Franklin's generator which built up an electric charge in the globe at the top

like substances, one acquires a positive charge and the other a negative charge, the kind of charge depending on the nature of the substances.

No matter how much one rubbed a glass or resin rod, the electricity was a fleeting affair—it lasted but a moment and was gone. Then E. C. von Kleist, a German clergyman and professor in the University of Leyden, using the friction electric machine, found a way to store electricity in a glass vessel filled with water. This came to be known as the *Leyden jar;* its electricity could be discharged at will.

Franklin was one of the scientists who began to play with this new toy, and he found a way to hook up several jars in series, the outside tinfoil coating of one jar being connected with the inside coating of the next. In this way he stored up a lot of electricity and obtained a bigger flash and a stronger shock when he discharged. In his famous kite experiment, Franklin collected electricity during a thunderstorm, charging a Leyden jar with the electricity from the clouds. Thus he showed that lightning was the same as the electricity produced by friction of glass and silk.

In 1767, Franklin's friend Joseph Priestley, the English scientist and clergyman who discovered oxygen, wrote a book called *History and Present State of Electricity*. Since this book was available in the State Library in Albany, Henry was probably up-to-date on what was then known about static electricity. He also owned a book by Abbé Nollet on the spark effects of the Leyden jar, a volume he later presented to the library of the Albany Institute.

The next chapter in the story of electricity was written by two Italian investigators. Luigi Galvani, an Italian anatomist, was dissecting a frog. His wife, who was helping him with his experiments, noticed that the frog's leg twitched violently when she touched its moist muscles with a scalpel. It happened that the leg lay close to an electrostatic machine on the table. We know today that the scalpel was merely the conductor that carried the electric spark from Galvani's generator to the leg and stimulated the muscles to contract.

Intrigued with his observations, Galvani continued with experiments that earned him the name of "Frog's Dancing Master" from those who didn't realize the importance of his work. But as he persisted, he found that he could make the frog's muscles twitch without the help of an electrostatic generator. In 1786 he attached the legs of a freshly killed frog to a copper hook and hung the hook over an iron railing.

When the legs touched the iron they twitched violently. Here was something new—electricity that was not generated by friction—but Galvani himself didn't realize just what it was. He thought that the frog's body was a naturally charged Leyden jar discharging electricity through the railing and the hook. Actually, he discovered the electric cell in which a current, since then known as a *galvanic* current, was generated by the chemical action of a cell or battery.

Nine years after Galvani published his work on "animal

Galvani's experiment. When the frog's leg touched the railing, the leg twitched in response to the current that flowed when the two unlike metals were brought into contact

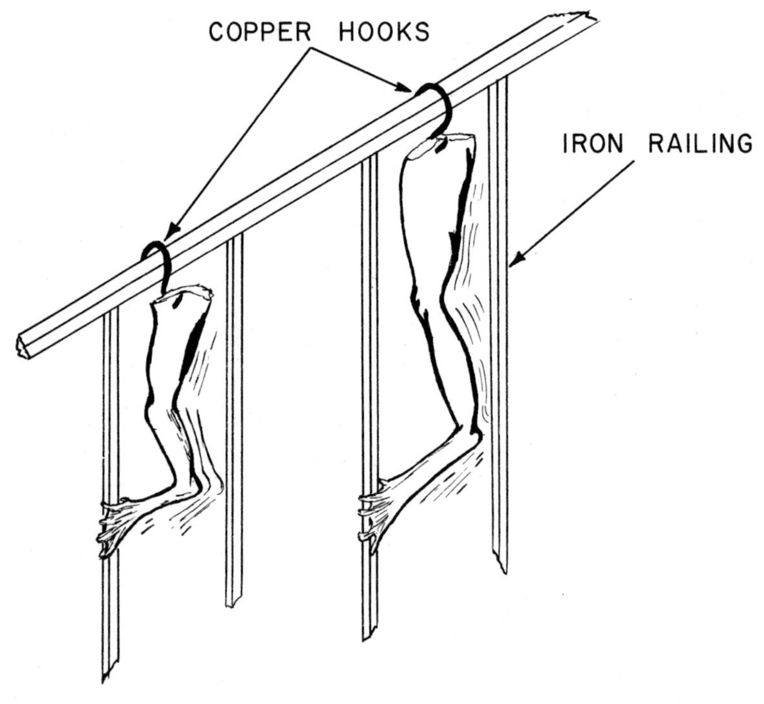

electricity," Count Alessandra Volta discovered that it was not electricity in the frog that caused the legs to twitch, but rather that two unlike metals in contact with each other produced an electric difference of potential.

Volta showed that when a copper plate and a zinc plate were in contact, they produced unlike charges. One plate had a positive charge, the other a negative charge. If these were placed on paper moistened with a salt solution and then connected at the opposite ends, a current of electricity flowed between them. In this way Volta made a battery—the voltaic cell, the first practical source of electric current! The frog's body was only a detector of the current—proof that it was flowing from the copper to the zinc through the frog's moist tissues, and then back to the copper plate.

Then Volta went on to build his *voltaic pile*. In 1800, in a letter to the Royal Society in London, he described how he produced continuous electricity. He erected a pile of alternate zinc and copper plates between which he placed pieces of moistened paper, until the pile was a foot high. Each pair of metal discs separated by the damp paper formed a cell with a difference of electrical potential. Together they made a battery. The higher the pile, the greater the difference of potential between the copper and zinc at the terminals of the pile, and the greater the shock discharged from it.

Modifying the powerhouse further, he built his Crown of Cups. Into a series of earthenware cups he placed alternate pieces of zinc and copper in a diluted solution of sulphuric acid. When the zinc of the first cup was connected to the copper of the last cup, a powerful current flowed. Instead of the fleeting spark discharges from the Leyden jar, a continuous source of current was now possible from a battery.

So, by the beginning of the nineteenth century it was

known that electricity took two forms: *static* which stands still, and *current* which flows. A *difference of potential* which may cause a current to flow, is measured in *volts,* the unit named after Volta, the first battery maker.

About magnetism it was known that the loadstone attracts metals, and that the magnetism of the earth deflects the compass needle. Sir William Gilbert showed that magnetism and electricity were different, and Franklin said there was no connection between them. "As to the magnetism that seems produced by electricity, my real opinion is that these two powers of nature have no affinity with each other, and that the apparent production of magnetism is primarily accidental," he wrote.

When Henry was still a student in the Albany Academy an important discovery was made which connected electricity in motion with magnetism.

Hans Christian Oersted, a Danish scientist, while demonstrating a lecture before his students in Copenhagen, accidentally rediscovered what had somehow gone unnoticed some twenty years earlier. On his table was a voltaic pile and a compass—which is really a magnetized needle. When a wire carrying an electric current was placed near the compass, the needle jerked violently. The young professor knew that magnets deflected compass needles, but now he found that electric current did the same thing. Also the stronger the current, the more powerful was the magnetic pull of the wire. Oersted's discovery was the beginning of the science of electromagnetism.

Prior to Oersted's discovery, it was known that like poles of two magnets repel each other (north repels north) but that opposite poles attract each other (north attracts south). André Marie Ampère, a French philosopher and mathematician, now

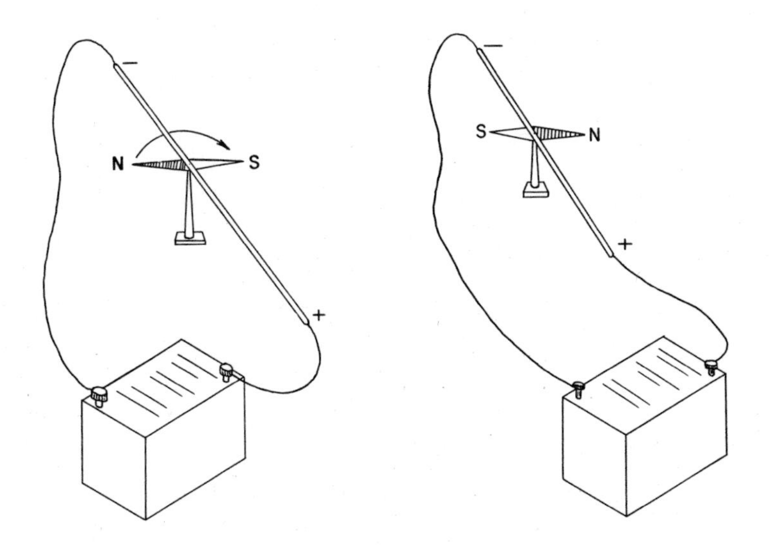

In Oersted's experiment the compass needle was deflected when placed near a wire carrying an electric current. The needle swings into a position at right angles to the wire

showed that magnetic fields generated by the flow of electricity through wires behaved similarly.

Ampère further discovered that coils of wire carrying electricity had north and south poles and behaved as permanent steel magnets. Also, since a magnetic field spreads out from a wire carrying electricity, if the wire is wound into a coil the magnetism is concentrated. It is on this principle that electric motors, and innumerable household electric devices are based.

Reports of this work going on in different parts of Europe very slowly filtered through to America. Some scientific journals from abroad occasionally reached scientists in the better established universities. James Freeman Dana in Dartmouth and Amos Eaton at Rensselaer were repeating the experiments.

Benjamin Silliman at Yale had started the *American Journal of Science,* the first important science publication in the United States.

Working in isolation and lacking the facilities of a leading institution, Henry yet kept his ear to the ground for such reports as he was able to examine. By chance he learned of a crucial experiment that had been performed in England which started him on the road to his own discovery.

In the summer of 1826, while Henry was preparing for his teaching duties, he took a trip to New York. Any other footloose young man with a little money in his pocket for the first time in his life, and time on his hands, would have used this visit to the Big City as a much-needed holiday. Perhaps he did some sightseeing, but since he carried a letter from Eaton to Dr. Renwick of Columbia College, he seemed to have one important purpose in making this trip.

Professor James Freeman Dana, on leave from Dartmouth, was lecturing at the College of Physicians and Surgeons, then located at Broadway and Barclay Street. There Henry was able to see one of the new electromagnets constructed by William Sturgeon of Woolwich, England. Henry promptly decided to construct one of his own as soon as he returned to Albany. From that moment he embarked on the road of original experimentation.

Sturgeon's electromagnet was a simple enough affair, hardly more than a high school student of today could construct with home-made equipment. The contraption consisted of a bar of soft iron bent into the shape of a horseshoe. To insulate it the bar was varnished, and a copper wire was wound loosely around it. The ends of the wire were dipped into cups of mercury connected to the positive and negative plates of a voltaic battery. When the circuit was closed, the current flowing through the wire magnetized the bar, and the electromagnet was capable of lifting a weight of nine pounds.

The young professor returned to Albany, his head buzzing with new ideas he had picked up in New York, itching to get to work—to repeat the experiment, and to see how Sturgeon's gadget could be improved upon. From the outset he was faced with limitations of his new job, the lack of time, equipment, space, and even the few pennies to buy supplies.

His teaching schedule called for seven hours a day in the classroom, part of the time devoted to drilling the younger boys in simple arithmetic. Hard and tedious work never fazed the quiet, modest young man, who accepted these routine duties with resignation. But he looked forward to the remaining hours when he taught physics, chemistry, and mathematics to the older boys—students whom he could infuse with his sense of adventure in the pursuit of science.

In addition to his regular school work he was still tutoring the shut-in, Henry James. And he found time for the meteorological investigations which were hardly more than the simplest observations of the changes in the weather. Farmers and seamen were then as now interested in its vagaries, but the forecasts were based on old wives' tales: a halo around the moon means rain; when the groundhog sees his shadow on February 2nd, winter will last another six weeks; and if it rains on St. Swithin's day it will rain for 40 days, and so on.

Henry tried to put some order into the odd information that amateur observers throughout the state had collected, by recording the weather conditions on days when wild birds and beasts, farm animals, and seeds of wild plants exhibited some curious behavior. These he set down in a table of Miscellaneous Observations, along with his readings of rainfall, wind direction, and temperature changes.

Lack of time alone would hardly have kept Henry from following his interest in the electromagnet. But where was he to do his experiments? Laboratories were an unheard-of luxury in the Academy. The room on the third floor where he conducted his classes was used from six in the morning on through the evening and its night classes. Even the simple materials needed to construct a battery were scarce, and one had to search through every general store for scraps of copper wire or mercury cups. If he could gather enough equipment, where would he store it? Besides, he had no funds. Deploring the fact that the exciting subject of electromagnetism was so sorely neglected, he pointed to the difficulty and expense of securing "a large galvanic battery."

The first year went by without even a beginning at the work he longed to do. His first chance came in August 1827, when school was out for one month. Then he had the lecture hall to himself and the time he hankered for. In the fall of that year he was ready with a paper that he read at the Albany Institute. Its title, "Some Modifications of the Electro-Magnetic Apparatus," suggests that he had begun to extend the subject which he said was "the most fruitful field of discovery."

Knowing his eagerness to share his knowledge and enthusiasm with his students, we can imagine him, when school reopened, trying out a demonstration in the classroom similar to this:

The students had settled themselves in the rows of wooden benches and were facing the professor behind his long table where, with the help of the more interested boys, he had gathered his apparatus.

Coming forward to the front of the table, as if to draw his pupils closer to him, he began his lecture:

"Today we will be talking about one of the most interesting

branches of human knowledge—the subject of electromagnetism. It is perhaps less generally understood in this country than almost any other field of natural science.

"Partly it is based on the principle discovered by Oersted. What is Oersted's principle, Benson?"

"I don't recall, sir, but isn't he the one who made a compass needle jump?"

"If he did, he must have been a magician. There is no magic in science," the professor said, ignoring the titters that greeted the boy's answer.

"The needle was attached by the magnetic force generated by a galvanic current," Rogers, in the back row, volunteered.

"Perhaps we ought to go back a little. What is galvanism, Maxwell?" Henry asked another student.

"Galvanism is electricity, moving electricity discharged from a chemical generator," Maxwell remembered from the previous day's lesson.

Henry walked back behind the table and pointing to a piece of apparatus, asked, "What is this instrument?"

"A voltaic cell," several boys answered in chorus.

"Well now, suppose I connect one wire to the copper plate and the other to the zinc plate of this battery, and attach the free ends to the switch. I close the switch. What happens?" Henry looked up expectantly for an answer.

"A galvanic current flows," the class repeated.

"But ah, how do we know? The wire looks the same whether the current is flowing or not."

Again someone recalled the previous demonstration, and offered to show the class how. The boy came up to the table, unhooked the wire from one plate, and held its end near but not touching the terminal. A spark jumped across the small air space.

"That is one way," the professor said approvingly. "But there is yet another way," and he proceeded to demonstrate.

Opening the switch, he reconnected the wire to the battery and closed the circuit. Then he held a small compass needle beneath the electrified wire. Immediately the needle swung back into a position at right angles to the wire. Then he placed the compass just above the wire, the needle swung completely around, until, again perpendicular to the wire, it was pointing in the opposite direction. Opening the switch, he repeated the experiment, but the needle did not move.

"Gentlemen, from this we must conclude that a wire carrying a current produces a magnetic field.

"Now suppose we reverse Oersted's experiment. Oersted placed a movable magnet near a wire fixed in position, but we will do an experiment with the magnet in a fixed position. For this experiment the earth will serve as our magnet."

While describing Ampère's experiment with a small ring of wire carrying a galvanic current, Henry was twisting a long wire into a rectangular coil, six inches by nine. He wrapped the coil in silk, and then suspended the insulated coil by a silk thread. The ends of the wire, previously soldered to a pair of small plates, hung from the bottom of the coil.

Pausing for a moment to get full attention, he went on. "I am going to dip the plates into this vessel containing dilute acid, while I beg you to fix your attention on the coil."

As he lowered the plates into the acid, the coil jiggled back and forth for a moment and then came to rest at right angles to the north-south meridian (equatorial position) of the earth.

The eyes of the class were glued to the remarkable electrified coil which, previously free to swing, was now held in a fixed position by the magnetic force of the earth.

"Now then, we see here positive proof that galvanism and magnetism are intimately connected. In the first instance, the freely movable compass needle was attracted by the magnetic force produced by the flow of current in the wire. In the latter, the freely movable coil carrying current was deflected toward the perpendicular position of the earth's magnetic meridian.

"The question we have to ask ourselves is how can we put this force to work, and with what instruments can we achieve this with the least amount of galvanism?"

It was Professor Henry's habit to leave his pupils with a vivid memory of the lesson, reinforced by the demonstration, and to raise in their minds a question over which to ponder before the next session.

Left: Sturgeon's magnet; *Center*: Henry's magnet;
Right: Henry's magnet with multiple coils

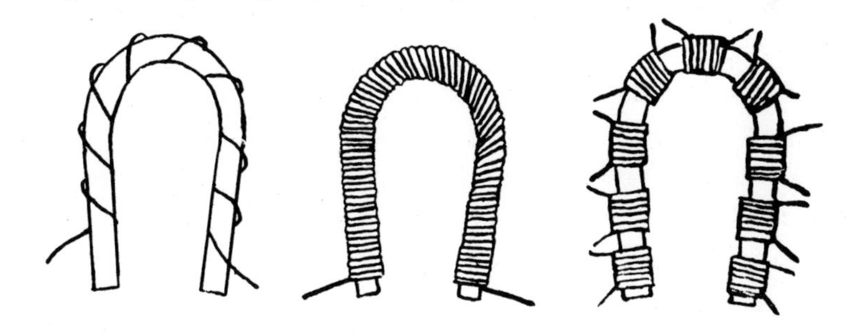

CHAPTER 4

Professor Turns Discoverer

FROM THE MOMENT Joseph Henry saw a model of Sturgeon's electromagnet, he wanted to improve its construction so as to increase its magnetic strength while reducing the quantity of current. From the very beginning he was an innovator. Thus, in his lecture in 1827, instead of using a single conducting wire, he wound many turns of wire into a coil. Soon the coil, made by winding 60 feet of wire on itself, was 20 inches in diameter.

Sturgeon varnished the surface of the soft iron bar, but Henry achieved much more effective insulation by wrapping the wire in silk. To avoid metallic contact between turns of the wire, Sturgeon used a loosely coiled strand of wire attached to a battery of 28 plates, each eight inches square. By insulating the wire, Henry was able to wind it tightly around the bar through many turns, and attach the two ends to only two small plates. (See center picture, page 59.)

In 1829 Henry exhibited an electromagnet made from a small piece of soft iron, a fourth of an inch in diameter, bent into the shape of a horseshoe. He wrapped 35 feet of insulated copper wire around the bar in 400 turns. Then he soldered the two little plates to the ends of the wire, which he dipped into a tumbler of dilute acid. In one of his early papers he explained:

> With these small plates the horseshoe became much more powerfully magnetic than another of the same size and wound in the usual manner, by the application of a battery composed of 28 plates of copper and zinc each 8 inches square.

The magnet lifted 28 pounds. (See right picture, page 59.)

By insulating the wire he achieved several things: he could wind the wire on itself through many turns; by arranging the coils at right angles to the axis of the core, he derived the full advantage of Ampère's observation that the electrically produced magnetism is strongest at a 90-degree angle to the core; by using more wire, he cut down on the size of the battery.

The end result was a much stronger magnet. He showed the way to change Sturgeon's toy electromagnet into a practical machine. From then on there was almost no limit to the size of the bar, the length of the wire, and the lifting power of the electromagnet. Henry's construction of the "spool" or "bobbin"—the form of coil used wherever an electromagnet is employed—was the first great contribution to the science of galvanic magnetization.

In the next few years he worked on the principle of achieving the strongest magnetism "with the least expense of galvanism"—another way of saying "with the greatest economy" in the current required.

Until 1830, Henry was still working under the difficult conditions of having to set up his apparatus during the summer vacation and dismantle it again when school reopened.

The spool or "bobbin" magnet

Yet he accomplished enough by demonstrating the superiority of his electromagnet over Sturgeon's to be granted the degree of Doctor of Law from Union College.

But more important to Henry: the Albany Academy gave him a basement room where he set up a laboratory of sorts. As a special gesture, a stove was provided so that he could work through the winter nights. With the laboratory, he was assigned an assistant, George W. Carpenter, a former student.

Strangely enough, the more Henry worked to perfect his instrument, the less he was inclined to publish his results. He kept at his solitary labor of love without much thought of seeking recognition. But time did not stand still.

While Henry was lost in his own world—narrow, but one that held deep secrets and many undiscovered truths—a Dutch scientist at Utrecht University was also playing with an electromagnet of the Sturgeon type. Gerard Moll, still using a single layer of wire, though wound more closely, constructed a magnet with a lifting power of 154 pounds. This he was able to do by using a powerful battery whose plates had a total surface of 1700 square feet. He reported his feat in the *Edinburgh Journal of Science*.

When Henry learned of Moll's work, late in 1830, he was jolted into reporting his own results, which were far in advance of Moll's. He sent his paper, along with a copy of Moll's, to Silliman's *American Journal of Science,* where they were printed side by side. The significant contribution of Henry—economy in the size of the battery—was expressed in its title: "On the Application of the Principle of the Galvanic Multiplier to Electro-Magnetic Apparatus, and also to the Development of the great Magnetic Power in soft Iron, with a small Galvanic Element."

In this article, Henry felt it his duty to point out his priority:

> The only effect Professor Moll's paper has had over these investigations, has been to hasten their publication: the principle on which they were instituted was known to us nearly two years since, and at that time exhibited to the Albany Institute.

Setting aside the question of who was first, the publication of their papers in January 1831 called public attention to the striking difference between Moll's and Henry's results: Moll's twelve-and-a-half inch magnet lifted 154 pounds, of which its maker was justly proud, but Henry's nine-and-a-half inch magnet lifted 750 pounds, nearly five times as much. But the most important contrast between the two was the different principle of construction—the enormous difference in battery power. Henry obtained his five-fold magnetic lift with one-eleventh of the quantity of current! This greater efficiency he achieved by the device of multiple winding of the multi-layer coil.

Henry called this his "quantity" magnet.

Summarizing the principle, he went on to say: "The multiplication of the wire increased the power in two ways: first by conducting a greater quantity of galvanism, and secondly . . . giving it a more proper direction . . ."—at right angles to the axis of the magnetic core.

The addition of a second coil exactly doubled the lifting power of the magnet. "The effect appears to depend in some degree on the number of turns," he wrote.

In the same paper he went on to describe another type of magnet which operated at a distance—the "intensity" magnet upon which the electromagnetic telegraph is based.

At least ten years before Henry's famous paper was published, Ampère had tried to send a current through wires connecting two distant stations, and found that the deflection of magnetic needles at the far end would produce "very simple and efficient signals for an instantaneous telegraph."

When this was reported to the Royal Academy of Science, Peter Barlow, an English mathematician and dabbler in magnetism, tried to repeat the performance. In 1825 he wrote: "I was therefore induced to make the trial; but I found such a sensible diminution with only 200 feet of wire, as at once to convince me of the impracticability of the scheme."

For a while this skepticism held back the progress of further work on a telegraphic system. But only for a while.

Henry was in the habit of repeating other people's experiments with an objectivity which often led him to discover a truth that had escaped previous attention. Reading Barlow's "project" very carefully he decided to try his hand at it.

The first problem, and one that nearly always stared him in the face, was getting the necessary supplies. Where was he to get hundreds of feet of insulated copper wire in Albany? The story is told that a friend—Dr. Philip Ten Eyck, a young man from one of the prominent Dutch families in the area—

came to Henry's aid. Somehow the wire was acquired, and Henry proceeded to carry out a famous experiment.

He began with a small electromagnet wound with about 8 feet of copper wire. Using in his battery a single pair of copper and zinc plates, 4 by 7 inches, he found that the magnet sustained four-and-a-half pounds. When he connected 500 feet of insulated copper wire between the battery and the magnet, its lifting power was reduced to two ounces—1/36th that without the long wire. When the length of the wire was doubled, the magnet lifted only half an ounce.

So far Barlow was right: "the magnetism was scarcely observable in the horseshoe," Henry remarked.

Then he was struck by an idea, just as three years earlier the notion of insulating the wire with silk had entered his mind. One evening, during a lull in a conversation with a friend, he jumped from his seat, struck the table with his hand, and shouted: "Tomorrow I shall make a famous experiment."

This story, told some fifty years later by Professor A. M. Mayer, must have made his friend look up in surprise, for it was unlike Henry to be either boastful or exuberant.

Once again, this time confronted with the failure of Barlow's experiment, he suddenly thought of a way out. He decided to use a different type of battery—one with 25 pairs of plates instead of a single pair. Substituting a battery of many small cells *connected in series* for the single large one used previously, he solved the problem of transmission through a long wire. He called this his "intensity" battery by which, as we know today, he created a circuit with much higher voltage. In this way he was able to send the current effectively through the enormous length of wire and still produce a signal at the other end.

As usual, Professor Henry was ready with a demonstration to his class in the fall of 1830.

Had we stepped into the lecture hall of the Albany Academy, we would probably not have recognized the scene as a class in session. The professor and several of his boys were climbing from bench to bench stringing wire around the walls of the room.

At the far end of the room, Dr. Ten Eyck, watching Henry for any change in instructions, was unreeling a huge coil of wire, and passing it along to the boys. He had often neglected his practice to come and assist the enthusiastic professor. But this morning promised to be a special demonstration for which he had supplied the wire, without knowing exactly what Henry had in mind.

"How much more wire do we have, Ten Eyck?"

"Keep going, there are two more turns to unwind."

"Well, we're over the measure. The line will be more than a mile," the professor said with great satisfaction.

The upper diagram shows batteries hooked up in series—Henry's "intensity" circuit; the lower shows the batteries in parallel connection—Henry's "quantity" circuit.

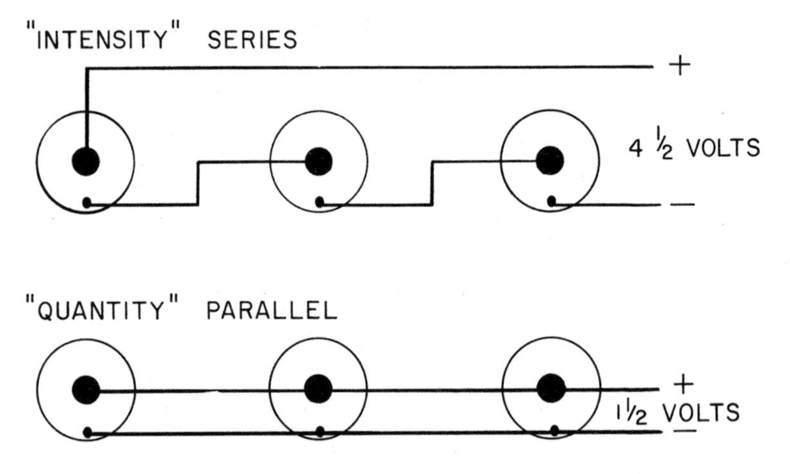

Henry's "quantity" battery

Finally, all the wire was strung many times around the room. Henry sent his assistants out, instructing them to tell the rest of the class to come in after ten minutes. Like Dr. Ten Eyck, the boys were mystified; they could sense from the elaborate preparations and the professor's face that they would witness a special show that morning.

Now, alone with Ten Eyck, he began to assemble his apparatus. First he set a little bell, mounted on a stand, on the window sill, where the two ends of wire encircling the room nearly met.

"Bring me the other pivot and the steel bar," he called.

He then carefully balanced the magnetized steel bar on the pivot, so that it was free to swing. Next he took a horseshoe-shaped iron core, on which he had spiraled several hundred turns of light wire.

Instructing Ten Eyck to arrange the horseshoe magnet so that its poles straddled one end of the steel bar, he himself went to the other end of the room to set up the battery. It was a long battery with 24 cells connected in series. Each cell was made of a pair of copper and zinc plates set in a vessel containing dilute acid. The copper plate of one cell was connected with the zinc plate of the next cell.

With a quick movement, Henry snapped the lowest rung of wire on the wall. Attaching one cut end to the end plate of the battery, he left the other dangling over a cup of mercury soldered to the far end of the battery.

The stage was set, and the boys filed into the room as if the curtain were just about to go up. They took their seats as Professor Henry took up his familiar place in front of the demonstration table.

"Vreeland, it is your turn to help with the demonstration. When I give the signal, connect the loose wire over the mercury cup."

Henry was not one to give the show away. First, he would build up the "plot" by reviewing what his audience already knew.

"Gentlemen, you will recall my demonstration with the quantity magnet that lifted 750 pounds. That magnet was made of wire wound one over the other around the soft iron core. The quantity battery to which the magnet was connected in circuit was made of a single 'pair,' and the copper and zinc plates were immersed in acid.

"You will also remember that this quantity magnet, attached to a quantity battery, while it lifted enormous weights, lost its magnetic power when a long wire was interposed between the battery and magnet. The current failed to flow over the 1,000 feet of wire.

"Just so, Barlow found that it lost its magnetism even over 200 feet of wire. This convinced him of the 'impracticability' of sending a signal over a distance. This morning we will prove him to be wrong.

"If you will now turn your attention to our magnet on the window, you will recognize it as the intensity magnet I constructed yesterday."

All eyes were on the horseshoe magnet with the single wire wound around it.

"You saw it demonstrated that this magnet had but little lifting power. But if you connect the intensity magnet with the intensity battery over there where Vreeland is standing, it will lift the same small weight at the end of a mile of wire as at a foot or two away."

He looked around the room, catching expressions of doubt, surprise, or assent, and said:

"I will now prove my contention. Vreeland, will you lower the wire into the mercury."

The circuit was closed.

At that moment the bell in the window rang, as the permanent magnet struck at it the instant it was repulsed by the electrified horseshoe magnet.

The class reacted as if it had received the shock from the current leaping across the mile of wire. Jumping out of their seats, they cheered, waved their caps, and applauded wildly.

When the excitement died down, Henry the actor, never forgetting his role as teacher, clinched his experiment:

"Gentlemen, you have just witnessed another manifestation of electromagnetism."

It was difficult to maintain order in the class. The boys were talking excitedly to each other, and a few shouted:

"This is instantaneous transmission! The Professor has invented a way to do it!"

Like the actor who tries to hush the applause of his enthusiastic audience with a gesture, Henry came forward to explain that he was not an inventor; he had only demonstrated a scientific principle. It would remain for someone else to apply it to a practical invention.

That someone else was, Samuel Finley Breese Morse.

Samuel Morse's knowledge of electricity began with his attendance at Professor Silliman's lectures in chemistry at Yale University. These included the subject of galvanism. But the boy had a talent for painting, and upon graduation in 1810 (he was then nineteen) he wrote home that he was really cut out to be an artist. Although his father had hoped that he would take up a learned profession, he agreed to let young Morse study painting with Washington Allston, who was going to England the following year.

In England, Allston introduced Morse to Benjamin West, the famous American portrait painter who had been living in London since 1763. West accepted him as a student and gave him special encouragement because he was an American. Morse made a name for himself during four years in England, and his work was shown at the exhibition of the Royal Academy.

In 1815 Morse returned home and opened a studio in Boston, hoping to get orders for portraits. During a year of waiting for painting commissions his active mind turned to invention. Together with his brother Sidney he invented a type of suction pump which, with a little alteration, could be used as a forcing pump in the fire engine. He secured a patent for it, but he continued with the idea of earning his livelihood from painting. He traveled from place to place seeking subjects for portraits and, from 1820 on, painted many famous people.

In 1827 Morse happened to attend a course of lectures on electromagnetism. The lecturer was none other than Professor Dana, from whom Joseph Henry had first learned about Sturgeon's electromagnet. Here Morse saw illustrated the power of a straight wire carrying a current of electricity to induce magnetism. Dana died shortly after giving these lectures, and Morse's interest in the subject temporarily lapsed.

In the meantime his success as an artist was established, and he became known among wealthy and influential people all over the East. He secured a number of commissions amounting to nearly three thousand dollars for pictures to be painted abroad, and in 1829 sailed for Italy to study the works of the old masters. He spent two years in Rome, a year in Paris, and then went on to London where he renewed his acquaintance with artists he had met during his earlier stay.

The story is told that on the return trip to America the idea of long-distance communication came to him. On board the packet *Sully* in October 1832, the conversation one evening turned to electromagnetism. Among the passengers was a doctor from Boston—Charles Thomas Jackson, one of the most talented and informed scientists of his time. He had with him some of the electrical apparatus of the type Faraday and Ampère were using, and was well acquainted with Professor Henry's work. Jackson remarked that electricity passed instantaneously over any known length of wire.

"How can you prove that?" a skeptical fellow passenger asked.

"Franklin tried to measure the speed of electricity in several miles of wire. But he could see no difference in time between the touch at one end and the appearance of the spark at the other," Jackson asserted.

At this point, Morse was reported to have commented: "If the presence of electricity can be made visible in any part of the circuit, I see no reason why intelligence may not be transmitted instantaneously by electricity."

From then on the idea of inventing an electric telegraph took complete possession of the painter. With commissions awaiting him, and a life of comfort, honor, and wealth before him, he chose to lay aside his painting for what turned out to be long years of poverty, toil, disappointment, and ridicule—the lot of a visionary. Living alone, sleeping on a cot, and often going hungry, he worked on his invention.

Those were frustrating years for the dedicated inventor. The fantastic contraption, here described in his own words, failed.

> My first instrument was made up of an old picture or canvas frame fastened to a table, the wheels of an old wooden clock moved by a weight to carry the paper forward, three wooden drums upon one of which the paper was wound . . . a wooden pendulum suspended to the top piece of the picture of the stretching frame and vibrating across the paper as it passed over the center wooden drum, a pencil at the lower end of the pendulum . . . an electromagnet fastened to a shelf across the picture . . . to an armature made fast to the pendulum. . . .
>
> Early in 1836, I procured forty feet of wire, and putting it in the circuit I found that my battery of one cup was not sufficient to work my instrument.

Had Joseph Henry been at his side he could have told him what was defective about his receiving apparatus. Henry's students at the Albany Academy had learned the secret of Barlow's failure, as they would now have recognized the reason for Morse's disappointment in his instrument.

Samuel Morse did not know of Henry's work, nor did he later fully appreciate its importance to his invention. But, luckily, one afternoon in January 1837, he consulted a colleague, Professor Leonard D. Gale, a chemist at the University who was familiar with Henry's experiments. Gale told the story later:

> I accompanied him to his room and there saw resting on a table a single-pair galvanic battery, an electromagnet, an arrangement of pencil, a paper-covered roller, pinion wheels, levers, etc. for making letters and figures to be used for sending and receiving words and sentences

Above: Reproduction of Henry's electrographic instrument; *Below*: Morse's experimental instrument

> through long distances . . . It was evident to me that the one large cup-battery of Morse should be made into ten or fifteen smaller ones to make it a battery of intensity.
>
> The remaining defect in the Morse machine as first seen by me was that the coil of wire around the poles of the electromagnet consisted of but a few turns only, while to give the greatest projectile power, the number of turns should be increased from tens to hundreds, as shown by Professor Henry in his paper published in the *American Journal of Science, 1831.*

After Gale helped Morse to arrange a battery of 20 cups and added "some hundred or more turns to the coil of wire" around the poles of the magnet, they succeeded in sending a message first through 200 feet, then through 1,000 feet of wire!

Many trials followed until Morse was able to record zigzag markings on paper, separated by spaces according to a code he worked out:

"215-36-2-58-112-04-01837" was the code for the phrase "successful experiment with telegraph, September 4, 1837."

A month or so later, Morse filed a patent application with the United States Patent Office. And in January 1838, he discarded the number signs for words, using an alphabet of dots and dashes, the Morse code. The new patent application also included the relay system of successive electromagnet circuits, first suggested by Henry.

Joseph Henry never tried to patent his discovery. Many years later when asked by Rev. S. B. Dod to give an account of his scientific work, he wrote about this matter:

> At the time of my making my original experiments on electromagnetism in Albany, I was urged by a friend to take out a patent, but this I declined, on the ground that I did not consider it compatible with the dignity of science

> to confine the benefits which might be derived from it to the exclusive use of any individual.

The granting of Morse's patent was temporarily held up while Morse went off to Europe where he hoped to interest financial backers in his invention. To his great disappointment, he received a cool reception in England, the home of the Wheatstone needle telegraph. Morse returned to the United States in 1839, and immediately sent off a letter to Henry, saying that he was coming to Princeton for a few days, and asking if Professor Henry could see him.

Besides explaining to Morse the difference between the quantity and intensity magnets, Henry encouraged the inventor, assuring him that he saw no reason why magnetization of soft iron should not occur at a distance of a hundred miles or more, provided the relay was inserted into the system. Henry had already given freely of his knowledge of this device to Wheatstone who used it in his needle telegraph.

Henry was equally unstinting in his help to Morse during the several years when Morse was trying to get Congress to appropriate the money for testing the telegraph system.

In 1842, Henry wrote to Morse from Princeton:

> My dear Sir: I am pleased to learn that you have again petitioned Congress in reference to your telegraph; and I most sincerely hope you will succeed in convincing our Representatives of the importance of the invention. . . . Science is now fully ripe for this application, and I have not the least doubt, if proper means be afforded, of the perfect success of the invention. The idea of transmitting intelligence to a distance by means of electrical action has been suggested by various persons . . . and unless some essential improvements have lately been made in . . . European plans, I should prefer the one invented by yourself.

On the eve of the closing date of the session, March 3, 1843, the Senate approved an appropriation of thirty thousand dollars to build a line over a distance of 40 miles from Washington to Baltimore.

On May 24, 1844, the first message was flashed over this wire. "WHAT HATH GOD WROUGHT?" it said.

In 1863, at the semi-centennial anniversary of the founding of the Albany Academy, Dr. Orlando Meads, a former student of Henry's, said in his address:

> Let us not forget that the click of the telegraph which is heard from every joint of those mystic wires which now link together every city, and village, and post, and camp, and station, all over this continent, is but the echo of that little bell which first sounded in that upper room of the Academy.

On December 17, 1924, a century and a half after Henry's birth, the little two-inch bell that figured in his discovery was taken from a case in the Albany Academy to be included as a major prop in the commemorative ceremony. Over the radio stations in Troy and Schenectady, its sound was broadcast among the speeches, which recalled for listeners throughout the United States the contribution of Joseph Henry in the field of electromagnetism.

Original bell used by Henry for his electrical telegraph

CHAPTER 5

Time to Get Married

JOSEPH HENRY had just passed his thirtieth year when he finished the first of his important experiments. In a very busy academic life he occasionally took time out for sociability. The handsome, genial young man was highly regarded by the scholars around Albany and Troy, but among those who were also proud to be his friends were members of the fashionable set. The young professor had brought honor to his city and its citizens, and his company was considered an asset at any social gathering. Friendly and personally charming, the serious student enjoyed these social contacts.

Henry always kept in close touch with his mother's family. His uncle, Alexander Alexander, was a well-to-do merchant in Schenectady. His son Stephen had graduated from Union College at the age of eighteen, with honors in mathematics and astronomy. He was invited to teach at the Academy, and their common interests drew the cousins together.

Henry visited the Alexander home in Schenectady as often as work and distance would permit. A romance was budding with his cousin Harriet, Stephen's sister. In the intervals between visits they corresponded.

The fragments of correspondence which remain suggest

Joseph Henry in his early thirties

that Joseph and Harriet had some understanding about a future union as early as February 1828.

"Mary Ann La Grange is with us at present," wrote Harriet, "to whom I have made some important disclosures but strange to tell she evinced no surprise."

And on Christmas Day, the following year, Joseph wrote to Harriet:

> . . .no Christmas since the days of my boyhood has ever appeared so pleasant in prospect as this.
>
> But now that it has come, instead of hastening to enjoy it with you as I fondly anticipated, I am unexpectedly obliged to embark in a few minutes for New York. My stay in that city, however, will be no longer than is necessary to transact some business for the Academy, and if nothing happens I shall probably be in your presence next

Wednesday evening, when I hope soon to lose in the pleasures of your company the recollection of every circumstance but the one in which I base my every hope of future happiness. . . .

Yours devotedly
Jos. Henry.

He was pleased when Harriet asked him now and then to buy her a few yards of cloth or a bonnet in fashionable Albany. Once he wrote her that if he couldn't settle the account in *"propria persona,"* he would "forward the cloth by the stage," and added, in the high-flown style of the day:

". . .If, at the time when I present the account, it should not be convenient for you to make immediate payment, I will accept as security of the debt, a bond and mortgage on your seal or *personal* property."

Then referring to some promise, ". . .when am I to have the pleasure of performing the one which depends on your coming to Albany? Do not delay too long as I am very anxious, as soon as possible, to completely retrieve my character and to reinstate myself in your good opinion as a person of strictest veracity."

Apologizing for taxing her patience with his scrawl (for all her cleverness in deciphering it), he adds that both Stephen and he could learn a lesson from her in the "art chirographical," a compliment to her beautiful handwriting.

Things did not always go smoothly, and there is evidence of stormy lovers' quarrels. After some misunderstanding, Joseph wrote her a penitent letter that reveals his gentleness, honesty, and philosophical turn of mind.

Albany, February 9, 1830

My dear Harriet:

Although our parting was rather colder than is compatible with that warmth of feeling, with which I always wish to regard you, and which I now find to be most essential to my own happiness, still I am confident, from a knowledge of your character, that you will not receive unkindly this communication, or be disposed to consider it an unnecessary intrusion. I know that you will believe it is only prompted by a sincere wish to dispel any unpleasant reflection, which my abrupt departure, and some previous improper expressions, may have left upon your mind.

Perhaps other feelings than those which now actuate me, may for a moment have suggested a sullen silence; but my Dear Harriet I value too highly those feelings with which I am happy in believing we mutually regard each other, to suffer them for an instant to be disturbed by an unmanly or improper reserve.

In reviewing our past intercourse, I find much to censure and to regret in my conduct; it has often been careless and inconsiderate: At first I treated you with much apparent coldness and reserve; and several times since I have acted with a rudeness, highly improper, towards the woman I love and respect. But this has not arisen from any want of a proper estimation of your worth, or from the slightest intention to manifest indifference, or disrespect; on the contrary, I have from the first regarded you with increasing esteem and affection, and have never intentionally or willingly given you either pain or offence. . . .

I should have guarded each word and each action. . . .

"A little thing can blast an infant blossom, and the breath of the South can shake the rings of the vine; . . . but when by time and consolidation, they stiffen into the hardness of a stem, they can then endure the storms of the North, and the rough blast, and the loud noise of a tempest and never be broken." [Apparently a quotation]

Precisely such in my opinion is the character of female attachment: At first every harsh word has the power to shake and alarm it; and the more tender its nature, the more sensitive it is to the slightest breath of suspicion

> or unkindness. But it does not always continue thus, for when constancy has been tested by experience longer than the *whims* of fancy can last or an unstable attachment, formed without esteem, can exist, the affection becomes confirmed, by confidence, as well as habit; and a quick reply, a trifling error, or even one unkind expression has no power to disturb it. . . .
>
> I may show for an instant a spirit of rebellion but one kind word, or one smile of reconciliation will I am sure never fail to call me back to my allegiance.
>
> Perhaps you will think me too confident and. . .somewhat mischievously inclined to put me to the trial—I am certain that I would stand the ordeal; but pray you in pity, do not unnecessarily give me the pain of the experiment.

Ending this long epistle, he begs for the favor of "but two lines" in reply—if she only knew what happiness this would bring him! A few days later, the forgiving Harriet comforted him with a gracious note:

> I can scarcely tell what at first displeased me. Some mere trifle which ought to have passed unheeded. Impute it not to any act of yours but to the inability of a temper which is often a difficulty. I regret the injury which I fear it has occasioned you, but I fear I should be half inclined to repeat the offence if I could be assured of its being followed by such a pleasing communication.

Feeling impelled to apologize for the "shortness" of her letter, she inquires about the correct use of the word.

And Professor Henry answered that it "may be used with grammatical as well as normal propriety," supporting this with a quotation and a reference to the Bard of Avon, who took similar liberties for the sake of brevity. But if this wasn't enough, he looked forward to discussing it further when they would meet on Saturday.

The house in Albany where Joseph and Harriet Henry lived. The number, 105, can be seen above the doorway

In the spring of the following year Joseph and Harriet were married. Then followed several months of separation, while Henry finished out the school year, made frequent trips to New York, and finally found a house for his bride at 105 Columbia Street, with a view of the State Capitol Building. Many letters showed the preoccupied Joseph struggling to find someone besides Nancy to see to cleaning the house and making it ready for the bride. It is not known whether his mother had died by this time; the only reference, in a footnote written after Henry's own death, is that she "lived to a good old age."

During these months of separation Henry wrote of his loneliness, assuring Harriet that in absence he could not forget that he was "a married man. . .which not even the active duties of my profession can repress. . ." He was confident that their union would be successful, because they had not "imagined perfections in each other which belong only to the beings of fiction and romance."

"We have cooly reflected on the trials and difficulties of the mate as well as warmly anticipated its enjoyments. . .I love you the more because you are not perfect. . . .I am sure you look upon my faults with an eye of extenuation."

From the very outset of their life together, tactful and self-effacing Harriet made few demands on Joseph's time, so that marriage, far from interfering with his work in the Academy laboratory, only made the busy days the more joyful.

Meanwhile, practical-minded men of industry had learned of Henry's ever stronger magnets. Could he construct them for immediate commercial use? His former teacher Amos Eaton, who was consultant to the Penfield Iron Works, recommended that the firm order two of the magnets to extract iron from pulverized ore. The magnets weighed only three pounds and were attached to two sets of cylinders of copper or zinc to be set in earthen quart mugs filled with dilute acid. The name of the little town at the site of the Penfield Iron Works was changed from Crown Point to Port Henry in honor of the maker of the magnets.

Thomas Davenport, a blacksmith from Brandon, Vermont, who later invented an unsuccessful electromagnetic machine, was so impressed with one of Henry's small magnets that he bought an extra one for seventy-five dollars. He described the wonder of it: ". . . as soon as the cups were immersed in the solution contained in the earthen mugs, the magnet adhered sufficiently strong to raise the anvil from the floor." Davenport invented a rotary motor, the first electromagnetic railroad car, and an electromagnetic piano-player, none of which achieved commercial use.

The Penfield Iron Works were the first to put the electromagnet to industrial use, but shortly afterwards came an order for a much larger and more powerful magnet for a university laboratory. Professor Benjamin Silliman, under whose leadership a famous school of science was growing up at Yale, ordered this one.

The Yale magnet weighed 59½ pounds, the horseshoe stood one foot high, and was wound with 26 strands of copper wire, each 31 feet long. It was insulated with cotton thread, the battery plates measured nearly five square feet, and it was capable of supporting the stupendous weight of 2,300 pounds!

Even Henry's smaller magnets had called forth unstinted praise from Sturgeon: "Professor Henry has been able to produce a magnetic force which completely eclipses every other in the whole annals of magnetism and no other parallel is to be found since the miraculous suspension of the celebrated oriental impostor in his iron coffin."

When the impressive Yale magnet was delivered, a description of it appeared in Silliman's *Journal* in April 1831. The editor added the comment: "It is eight times more powerful than any magnet hitherto known in Europe."

Indeed, news of it traveled abroad, despite the fact that European scientists still looked down their noses at the achievements in America. If some thought that America was still a land of barbarians, Henry's work didn't escape the English physicist Michael Faraday, who had a similar giant "quantity" magnet built for his laboratory.

And in France a young professor, Claude Servais Mathew Pouillet, was literally almost thrown off his feet while demonstrating a Henry magnet. Wishing to show his students that the magnetic power is lost when the circuit is broken, he opened the switch with his bare hands and received a violent shock.

Little did the embarrassed Pouillet suspect that the violence of the shock was due to *self-induction,* for the discovery of this property of electrified magnets was yet to come.

CHAPTER 6

Sparks from a Magnet

I HAVE LATELY succeeded in producing motion in a little machine by a power which I believe has never before been applied in mechanics—by magnetic attraction and repulsion," Henry announced, in Silliman's *American Journal of Science*, July 1831.

Then he described his invention of the first electromagnetic engine. His "little machine" consisted of a horizontal electromagnet that rested on a vertical pivot and across the poles of two upright permanent magnets. The strands of insulated copper wire extending from the electromagnet at each end were bent downward to dip into mercury thimbles in connection with the plates of two batteries.

The electromagnet was free to teeter on the pivot like the ends of a see-saw. When the electromagnet was tipped, contact was made with the battery on the low side, while the other end became disconnected. The current from the battery with which the magnet was connected then flowed through the coiled wire, producing electromagnetism in the movable magnet so as to tip it in the other direction. As soon as it had been tipped the other way, the connections with the first battery were broken and those with the second battery established.

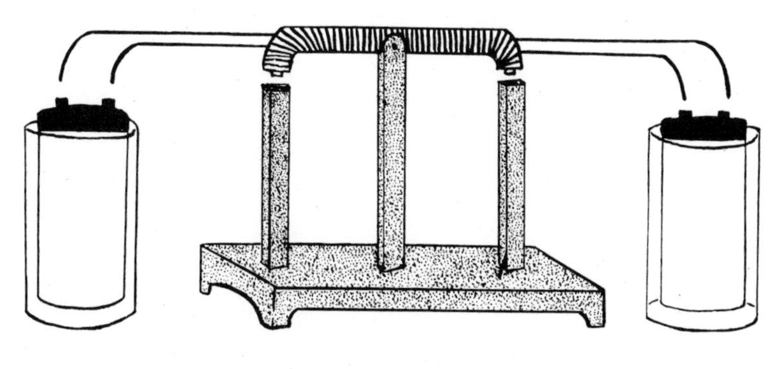

Above: Design for Henry's electromagnetic engine; *Below*: The actual machine

The magnetism was thus reversed, causing the electromagnet to move in the opposite direction.

This oscillation back and forth at the rate of 75 times a minute went on for an hour or more, or for as long as the battery lasted.

Describing the operation of the little electromagnetic engine, Henry went on to say that he didn't attach much importance to his invention, "since the article in its present state can only be considered a philosophical toy; although in the progress of discovery and invention it is impossible that the same principle . . . on a more extended scale may hereafter be applied to some useful purpose."

With his usual reticence, Henry was pointing to the future when every electric motor—the starter of an automobile, the electric engine of a train or trolley car, and the myriads of electric machines employed in factory and home—would be built on the principle of his "philosophical toy."

But for Henry it held interest only insofar as it demonstrated a principle. He had no desire to apply his knowledge to practical machines, still less to patent his discoveries. He wished only to add to the world's knowledge, satisfied to leave to others the business of applying the principles he discovered.

Some years later when he was a professor at Princeton he deplored the American practice of honoring only "those who simply apply known facts rather than the ones who *discover* new principles." He must have been amused when long after he had left Albany a dealer in apparatus offered to sell him a simple machine like the one he himself had originally built. Henry patiently brought out his own early model. The bogus inventor, pointing out what he thought were its flaws, warned the professor that he had better not construct any more of this kind, lest he infringe on the dealer's patent rights. . . .

In August 1831, Henry, making the most of his precious month's vacation, planned a new experiment in the "identity of electricity and magnetism." To this day it is not known

Henry's coils, probably intended for the construction of a dynamo

exactly what he had in mind, but word spread that he was forging a magnet twice the weight and power of the Yale College magnet. And George Carpenter, his assistant, recalled much later that Henry told him he had drawn a spark from a magnet.

When Benjamin Silliman learned about the project, he wrote Henry asking for more details. Henry replied weeks later that he had been working on an "extensive plan," but had been forced to abandon the project for the moment.

"I had partially finished a magnet much larger than any before made, and have constructed a kind of reel on which more than a mile of copper wire was wound. I was obliged to abandon the experiments on account of the room in which my apparatus was erected being wanted for the use of the Academy and it was not convenient for me to resume them during the winter."

It is a pretty good guess that Henry, like physicists in Europe, must have asked the question: if electricity magnetizes, why won't magnetism electrify? And so while nobody knows for sure it is possible that Henry's "extensive plan" may have been to construct a dynamo. But while the Albany professor packed away his equipment for the school year, a physicist overseas was searching for a way to convert magnetism into electricity.

Without knowing it at the time, Henry had a mighty rival in Michael Faraday. And by one of those quirks of history the lives of the two men ran a somewhat parallel course. Faraday, born in 1791, was eight years older than Henry, and by 1830 had not yet made his major discovery. Like Henry, he was self-taught. The son of a blacksmith, he had no more chance at a formal education than Henry. Even more than in America, education in England was a luxury not meant for a poor boy. Like his father he had to learn a trade and work with his hands.

At thirteen, Michael was apprenticed to a bookbinder, after a year's trial of making himself generally useful to Riebau, the owner of the bindery. Since Michael had performed his duties as errand boy satisfactorily, he was signed up for seven years. A likable boy, he worked his way into the heart of his master, who saw no harm in the boy's looking inside the books he bound.

One day Michael came upon an article on electricity in the *Encyclopedia Britannica.* It told about the work of Galvani and Volta, von Kleist and Franklin. It didn't take the boy long to find out the little that was then known about electricity. The world of chemistry proved even more fascinating when he came across Mrs. Marcet's *Conversations in Chemistry,* which described some chemical experiments. Michael saved a few shillings to buy some scanty apparatus with which to repeat the experiments he had read about, and to train himself in laboratory ways. Skillful in handling simple experiments, he gloried in every one that came out just as the book said it would.

Talking one day with a customer in the bindery, Michael confided that he longed to attend one of Sir Humphry Davy's lectures at the Royal Institution. It was preposterous that a bookbinder's apprentice should want to hear the famous chemist who had discovered laughing gas, but the customer promised to get him a seat in the gallery. The price would be a few shillings, but for the privilege of attending four lectures on science the expenditure was more than worth it to young Michael.

He listened to the lectures intently, writing with frantic haste, and then at home in his dingy little room stayed up late into the night laboring over his notes, getting all the meaning he could from them. What a thrill to know that he could make sense out of what he had heard and put down in his own words!

Riebau was tolerant of his apprentice's eager absorption with the inside of the books he bound, but the time came when the apprentice was ready to take up his craft in the De La Roche Bindery. His new boss would not stand for such nonsense; he had hired Michael to turn out books and not to steal off to some corner to read.

Once he had peeked into the world of science, Faraday was unhappy in his trade. He dreamed of leaving the bindery and becoming a scientist. But what did he know? He had no schooling, no knowledge of mathematics, neither money nor influence to get into that palace of learning, a laboratory. But Faraday had courage—some people would have called it brazenness. There must be a way to get to the great Sir Humphry Davy!

He wrote Davy a letter, enclosing his careful notes of the chemist's lectures, which he sent as "proof of my earnestness." Then he waited and hoped. After all, it was a daring thing to do, to approach so popular and world-famous a scientist.

One morning a month later a liveried carriage stopped at Faraday's poor home on Weymouth Street. Mrs. Faraday could hardly believe that the footman had not stopped at the wrong door. But no, he came with a message from Davy to her son. He was to present himself to Sir Humphry at the Royal Institution the next morning.

Michael was there on time, of course. He could hardly believe his luck when Davy told him he needed an assistant in the laboratory, and Faraday could have the job at twenty-five shillings a week, if he wanted to leave bookbinding. The door into a new, exciting life was thus opened to Faraday, and Davy was headed for what he later said was his greatest discovery—Michael Faraday.

Faraday was twenty-two when he began as an apprentice in science, starting from the lowest rung—glassware washer and valet to Davy. His adventures in chemistry that eventually led to his appointment as director of the laboratory at the Royal Institution are part of a success story which has been told elsewhere.*

Through those years and up to 1830, Faraday, like Henry, renounced the lure of financial offers to be a consultant to firms dealing in benzine, which was then being produced in quantities. Neither he nor his wife, Sarah, had any desire for wealth. They were satisfied with his small salary at the

*Michael Faraday; from errand boy to master physicist by Harry Sootin, Messner, 1954.

Institution, that offered opportunities for experimentation, and for the genius, provided the chance of charting new paths to scientific knowledge.

Faraday was nearly forty when scientists were buzzing with the wonders of electromagnets. While the world was full of magnetism, or so it seemed, with the earth itself a giant magnet, electricity still came from the voltaic battery that was easily burned out. What a wonderful source of energy electricity would be if it could be made in quantity! It was natural for Faraday to wonder about converting magnetism into electricity, even though decades before Franklin had said there was no connection between them.

The scientific world in 1830 had known for ten years that a copper wire wound around an iron core and carrying a current became a magnet. Could the magnet be induced to set up a current in the wire? This is the problem that Faraday brooded over and tried to bring to a solution.

For seven years Faraday had been experimenting, trying to produce electricity, but time after time he failed, possibly because his battery was too weak or his instrument too insensitive to detect it. Then in 1831 he began all over again with a stronger magnet like Henry's. He made a ring of soft iron around which he wound two coils. Passing a current through the first, he connected the second to a galvanometer, an instrument with a swinging needle that is deflected when a current passes through it. When the battery circuit was closed, he noticed that the galvanometer needle jumped. Then he opened the circuit, and the same thing happened, except that when the circuit was broken, the needle was deflected in the opposite direction. But he didn't realize that he had discovered what he had been searching for.

Several weeks later he began all over again. Perhaps the

meaning of the experiment began to dawn on him. He wrote: "I am busy just now on electro-magnetism, and I think I have got hold of a good thing but can't say. It may be a weed instead of a fish, that after all my labor, I may at last pull up."

This time he used a straight bar instead of a ring, rapidly thrusting the bar magnet through a coil of wire. When the bar was in motion, electricity passed through the coil. He reported his results to the Royal Society late in the fall of 1831, and an abstract of it appeared in the *Library of Useful Knowledge,* of December 12, 1831. In part the account read:

> If a wire connected at both extremities with a galvanometer be coiled, in the form of a helix [coil or spiral] around a magnet, *no current* of electricity takes place in it . . . But if the magnet be withdrawn from or introduced into such a helix, a current of electricity is produced *whilst the magnet is in motion,* and is rendered evident by the deflection of the galvanometer. . . . Thus is obtained the result so long sought after—the conversion of magnetism into electricity.

Once more Joseph Henry was forestalled by prior announcement of a discovery he had also made! Not having Faraday's opportunity to continue his work unhampered, since his experiments were interrupted periodically by his teaching duties, Henry had delayed publishing, perhaps hoping to clinch his experiments by repetition. Or, it may have been simply a result of his exasperating indecision.

When Joseph Henry learned of Faraday's results from an abstract of the Royal Institution *Proceedings,* he quickly assembled his notes and dispatched an article to Silliman's *Journal.* The July issue was in press, but Professor Silliman, grasping the full significance of the paper, printed it as an addendum to the issue. Its title was "On the Production of Currents and Sparks of Electricity and Magnetism."

Henry explained that before knowing of Faraday's experiment he "had succeeded in producing electrical effects in the . . . manner, which differs from that employed by Mr. Faraday, and which appears to me to develop some new and interesting facts."

Then he went on to describe how he set up a huge magnet; an armature wound with wire was placed in position across the ends of the magnet and fastened so that there was no motion. The two projecting ends of the helix were dropped into two cups of mercury, and connected to a distant galvanometer by two copper wires each about forty feet long.

"This arrangement being completed, I stationed myself near the galvanometer and directed an assistant at a given word to immerse suddenly, in a vessel of dilute acid, the galvanic battery attached to the magnet. At the instant of immersion, the north end of the needle [of the galvanometer] was deflected 30° to the west, indicating a current of electricity from the helix surrounding the armature."

In other words, when the galvanic circuit was closed the iron bar became magnetized, and *induced* an electric current in the previously "dead" wire around the armature. In this manner Henry converted magnetism into electricity, or as we would say today, created an induced current. Instead of coming from a battery, the current now came from the electrified wire to the magnet whose lines of force were perpendicular to it.

Further, he noticed that: "That effect however, appeared only as a single impulse, for the needle, after a few oscillations, resumed its former undisturbed position . . . although the galvanic action of the battery, and consequently the magnetic power, was still continued."

Then he proceeded to break the galvanic circuit by re-

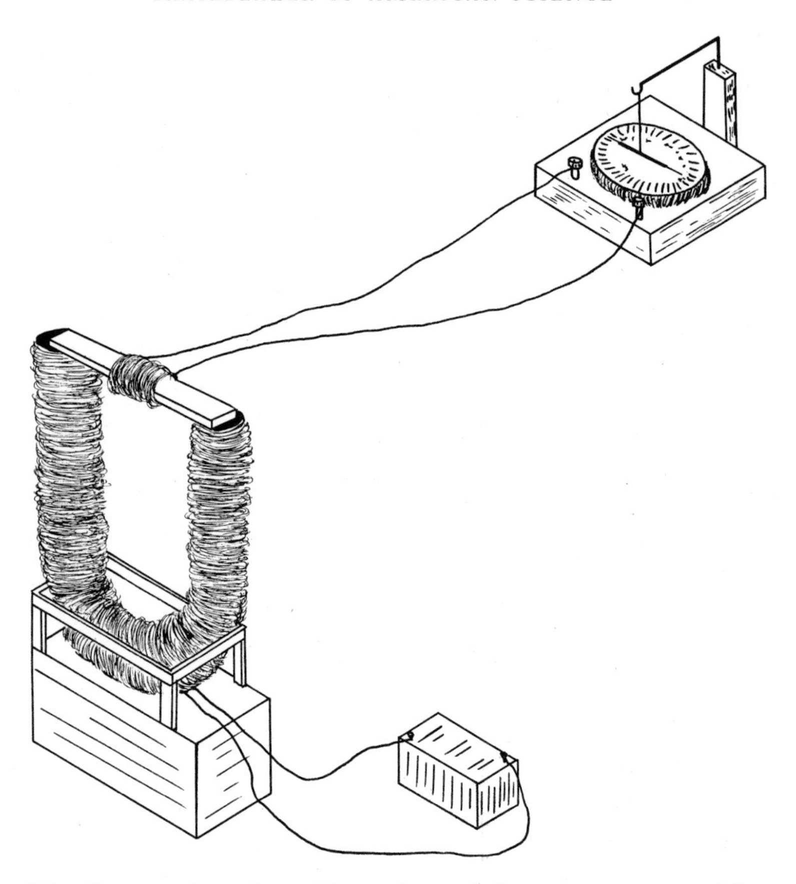

The diagram shows how Henry detected the current generated by his horseshoe magnet. The magnet is connected with the battery (bottom right). Across its poles is the armature coil in which the current is induced. At the top right is the galvanometer. The deflection of its needle shows the passage of current

moving the plates from the acid, and at that instant something he hadn't expected occurred.

"I was however much surprised to see the needle suddenly

deflected from a state of rest to about 20 degrees to the east, or in the contrary direction, when the battery was withdrawn from the acid, and again deflected to the west when it was reimmersed."

Explaining what he saw, he described this transformation of energy in these words:

> In the first place, magnetism is developed in the soft iron of the galvanic magnet by the action of the currents of electricity from the battery, and secondly, rendered magnetic by contact with the poles of the magnet, induces in its turn currents of electricity in the helix which surrounds it; we have thus as it were electricity converted into magnetism and this magnetism again into electricity.

Henry and Faraday went about their independent discovery of the phenomenon of induction in somewhat different ways, but the principle was essentially the same. Since in Henry's experiment the magnet was stationary, he thought that his own performance was different from Faraday's. Henry induced the current by making and breaking the circuit, while Faraday accomplished the same thing by moving the magnet. But both men discovered electromagnetic induction!

Thanks to their discovery we today have the electric motor, induction coil, transformer, and the giant dynamos that run our factories and light our streets and homes. Whether the huge coils of wire are turned between powerful electromagnets by steam engine, waterpower, or turbine, the wires cut across lines of magnetic force first in one direction, then in the other, producing electricity.

Keen as Henry's disappointment must have been to have had his priority snatched from him, he never made public claim to his own discovery. Instead he congratulated Michael Faraday as first discoverer of magneto-electricity. He set aside personal pride for the greater satisfaction of gaining new and deeper insight into a fundamental phenomenon of nature.

In the privacy of his family and among his close friends he voiced his disappointment. His daughter Mary later said that a friend had written her: "Your father often spoke to me of his disappointment about that discovery. 'I ought to have published earlier,' he used to say. 'I ought to have published, but I had so little time, and how could I know that another man on the other side of the Atlantic was busy with the same thing?' "

If, in modern histories of science, Henry's independent discovery of induction is more often omitted than acknowledged, one additional observation of his is fully attributed to him.

The discovery with which he alone is credited is that of *self-induction,* which he described in 1832.

When the poles of a battery were connected with copper wire not more than a foot in length, no spark was noted when the circuit was either opened or closed. But if instead of a short wire, one of thirty feet or more was used and the circuit broken, "by drawing one end of the wire from its cup of mercury, a vivid spark is produced. . . . The effect appears somewhat increased by coiling the wire into a helix: it seems also to depend in some measure on the length and thickness of the wire."

Explaining this, he said that he could account for it "only by supposing the long wire to become charged with electricity by which its reaction on itself projects a spark when the connection is broken." It is as if the current which develops slowly when the circuit is closed achieves a high voltage, or becomes an "intensity" current, which "flows on" after the circuit is broken. This phenomenon of self-induction or "extra current" is produced by induction on itself when the circuit is broken, and self-induction opposes the dying out of the current. It is self-induction that accounts for the flash that is seen when a trolley pole jumps its cable. This was the cause of the startling shock received by Pouillet while breaking the circuit of the powerful electromagnet which he demonstrated to his class that very year.

Perhaps the scientific community in which he lived felt more let down when their highly regarded professor was forestalled, than he did himself. At least so it seemed to the sensitive young professor who had such an overpowering sense of duty. Doubtless his failure to "stake out" his scientific claim deprived the still young nation of the glory that comes with a great discovery. Had Henry received his just acknowledgment, American science would have been given a much-needed stimulus to further advancement.

Henry seemed to feel that his friends silently reproached him for his dilatoriness. Those like Dr. Ten Eyck, who helped him get necessary supplies for his experiments, might well have been dispirited by the withdrawal of his claim to discovery.

Dr. James C. Welling, president of Columbia University, speaking about this after Henry's death related: ". . . in the midst of the fervors which had come to quicken his genius, he was visited by the fancy (or was it a fact?) that a few of the friends who had hitherto supported him in his high ambition were now beginning to look a little less warmly on his aspirations."

If so, not all his friends deserted him. William Dunlap, theater manager, novelist, playwright, painter, and warm admirer of Henry, thought it necessary to reassure his despondent friend. One day when they were together on a Hudson River steamboat, Dunlap, noting the sadness on the professor's face,

Joseph Henry statue in front of the old Albany Academy

laid his hand affectionately on his shoulder, and said, "Albany will one day be proud of her son."

In the years to come the prophecy came true. A statue graces the front of the Albany Academy—now The Joseph Henry Memorial—in a park adjoining the Capitol. A replica of the statue stands in the Hall of Science in the State Museum, as if guarding, in the glass case next to it, the few Henry relics that remain.

In the designation of the induction unit, Henry's name became immortalized along with those of Ampère, Galvani, Volta, Faraday, and Ohm. In 1893, the International Congress of Electricians met in Chicago. Ironically the proposal to honor Henry came not from an American, but from a Frenchman and an Englishman. The unit of inductance was designated as the "henry."

Just as the *volt* is the unit of electromotive force (electrical pressure), the *ampere* the unit of current strength (rate of flow), the *henry* is the unit of inductance (the rate of change) of current per second.

Henry's brilliant work at the Albany Academy did not bring public acclaim. Too few people could appreciate the importance of his major discovery—electrical induction. The wealthy parents of his pupils knew him only as a faithful and competent teacher. The average citizen knew even less about him. Only the few physicists with whom he was in contact through his correspondence and publications recognized his worth. In this narrow circle he had made a name for himself as an outstanding experimenter and a great lecturer.

Fortunately, just at the time when Henry seemed to have outgrown his native town and the Academy to which he had devoted six memorable years, the College of New Jersey at

Princeton had a vacancy. The trustees were in search of a professor to fill the chair of natural philosophy, and his scientist friends proposed Joseph Henry for the post.

Dr. John Maclean, the college president, wrote to Henry to inquire about his availability. In reply, Henry confided his reasons for wishing to leave the Academy. He said that he was not unhappy with his situation, and that he had received good treatment from the authorities. However, teaching sixty boys the rudiments of mathematics on a seven-hour-a-day schedule left him no free time for his researches.

With his customary modesty, he went on:

"Are you aware of the fact that I am not a graduate of any college and that I am principally self-educated?"

Though he did mention his honorary degree from Union College and the fact that he was a corresponding member of the Royal Physical Society of Edinburgh, Henry added drily that such honors "are cheaply purchased."

The formal nomination was made by Dr. John Torrey, a professor of chemistry at Princeton, and by Dr. Jacob Green, an alumnus and the son of Princeton's former president Ashbel Green. Green, himself a student of electromagnetism, was familiar with Henry's work, and at the time of the nomination was teaching at Jefferson Medical College at Philadelphia.

When Maclean asked Torrey about Henry's qualifications for the post, he replied: "Yes, he is the very man for you. He can fill my place, too."

But when Henry's name was laid before the board of trustees, one of them, betraying his ignorance of the nominee's accomplishments in science, asked "Who is Henry?"

The answer came from those who were aware of Henry's work, and had recommended him in the first place. Urging his appointment, Professor Benjamin Silliman of Yale wrote:

"Henry has no superior among the scientific men of the country," and Professor James Renwick of Columbia College unqualifiedly said: "Henry has no equal."

Professor Henry was unanimously elected. With full appreciation of the opportunities for research and leadership in a great institution, he gladly accepted the appointment.

With his departure from the Academy and its limitations, a period rich in accomplishment and happiness began for the great physicist.

That he added luster to the college and distinction to its faculty was never doubted then or later. Many years afterward, when one of the college presidents was asked what makes a great university, he answered that the first requirement is the influence of such inspiring and illustrious teachers as Joseph Henry. The college's pride in Henry was destined to grow with time.

CHAPTER 7

To Nassau Hall

ONE RAW DAY in November 1832, the Henrys and their year-old son Willie, left Albany for good. To the young scientist, the wrench of parting from his family and friends was softened by the expectation that there would be visits back and forth in the years to come. He could stride ahead rapidly now that he had left the bumpy country lane of his earlier career for the veritable highroad of learning.

The College of New Jersey, founded in 1746 by Presbyterians, to train students for the ministry, was the fourth college in colonial America. It had achieved distinction from the start because of its enlightened and liberal educators, some of whom had been invited from Scotland and England. By the time Benjamin Franklin launched the American Age of Enlightenment his widening sphere of influence touched also the prosperous and cultured families around Princeton, whose sons attended the college. For Henry it was a great step from a provincial academy to a university with an honored tradition of learning.

The college (which became Princeton University in 1896) offered him exactly what he had long needed. He was given a laboratory which was his to use the year round—no more interrupting of crucial experiments for simple lack of space! There was an allowance for supplies for his experiments, which he could buy on trips to nearby New York or Philadelphia. There was a newly opened railroad to the latter city, which offered the stimulation of the American Philosophical Society founded by Franklin in 1743, and of the younger Franklin Institute which specialized in scientific studies.

The College authorities recognized the distinction that Henry was bringing to Princeton, and paid him the maximum salary of $1,000 a year. True, he was often given only half that sum, when college finances were low, and he sometimes bought apparatus out of his salary.

But Joseph and Harriet received high dividends in other coin than money. They lived in a pleasant, spacious town and enjoyed the companionship of delightful faculty families. Their own family was growing; their daughter Mary was born about two years after they arrived, followed by another girl. Harriet called her "our little pup." It is not known whether this was Helen, or one of the two Henry children who died in babyhood. Willie, the son and heir, was "Bub." After a few years in Princeton the Henrys moved into a fine brick house which the college built for them after Henry's own design. (This house, on the Princeton campus, is now the residence of the current dean.)

A further source of happiness was the arrival of Harriet's brother, Stephen Alexander, who had received an appointment as Professor of Astronomy. Just as Joseph Henry had welcomed his cousin Stephen to the faculty of the Albany Academy, he was now proud to have him in Princeton as brother-in-law and brother in science. The relation between the two young scientists had always been close, and was enriched, as it had been in Albany, by shared interests. On many

Stephen Alexander (Joseph Henry's brother-in-law)

a cloudless night, Henry and Alexander happily collaborated in experiments in astronomy.

Henry often said that his years at the University were the happiest in his life. He had left behind the heartaches of the Academy, and had not yet felt the burdens of administration that were to fall on his shoulders in later years. Ever in search of new truths, he found a haven in these scholarly surroundings. Eager to impart his own enthusiasm, he was stimulated by the response of appreciative students.

He was assigned a room on the third floor of Philosophical

Hall. This building, long since demolished, occupied a prominent place on the campus, opposite Stanhope Hall, its identical twin, still standing. The glass-enclosed shelves in his laboratory displayed one of his earliest electromagnets and the machine with which he demonstrated mechanical motion produced by alternating electromagnetic discharges. To these symbols of his earlier work he added new tools with which he enriched the knowledge of electromagnetic principles.

During the first year his teaching schedule was difficult. In addition to his classes in natural philosophy he was asked to take over those of Dr. Torrey, who confidently went off on a visit to Europe during that year. This meant that Henry had to teach also chemistry, mineralogy, and geology. Later he was assigned, in addition, the lectures in astronomy and even those in architecture. No wonder that the faculty admired their new colleague for his versatility and for his

Philosophical Hall at Princeton

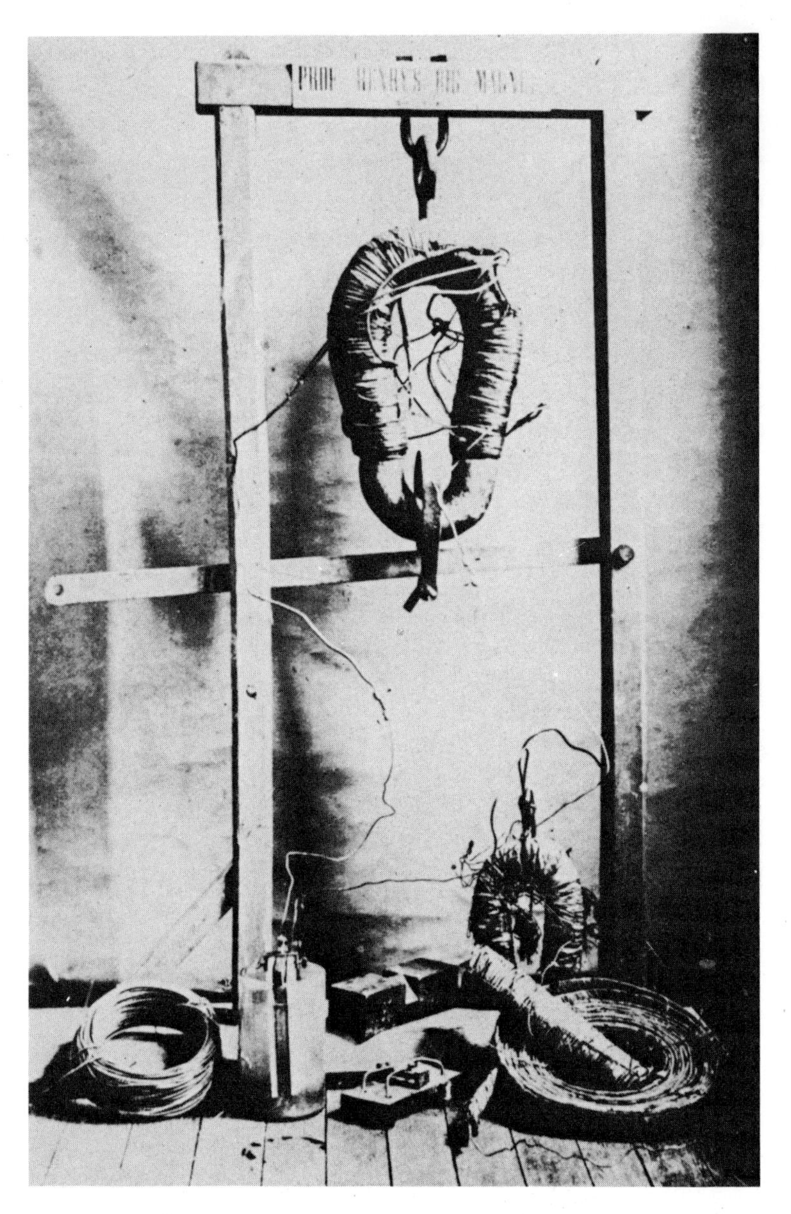

Big Ben, Henry's electromagnet at Princeton

gracious willingness to substitute for them during their leaves from the college.

Despite these heavy classroom duties, Henry managed to work on original experiments. He was determined to construct a magnet—this time for his own use—that would eclipse the one he had made for Silliman at Yale. The Princeton giant, which the students christened Big Ben, sustained a weight of 3,500 pounds, which delighted the ardent professor. One of his students who was present at its completion told about the event: "We shall always remember the intense eagerness with which he superintended and watched the preparations, and how he fairly leaped from the floor in excitement when he saw his instrument suspending and holding a weight of more than a ton and a half."

The colossal magnet was designed only to enable Henry to continue his researches with the best possible apparatus. He had no wish to outdo other scientists.

While still at Albany, Henry had lectured on the electrical "relay" to make possible long-distance electromagnetic telegraphing. The idea of the relay was to introduce into the circuit a second horseshoe coil of the "intensity" type with its own intensity battery.

Soon after coming to Princeton, he constructed a telegraphic system, when none existed anywhere in the world. It was in this project that he used his giant magnet. In a letter to Rev. S. B. Dod many years later he wrote: "As soon as I became fully settled in the chair which I occupied, I recommenced my investigations, constructed a still more powerful electromagnet than I had made before—one which would sustain over three thousand pounds—and with it illustrated to my class the manner in which a large amount of power might, by means of a relay magnet, be called into operation at the distance of many miles."

The new telegraph for which he strung up the wire across the campus contained the innovation of the relay; also he completed the circuit by sinking the ends of the wire into the earth. In the same letter to Dod, he described it in these words:

"I think the first actual line of telegraph using the earth as a conductor was made in the beginning of 1836. A wire was extended across the front campus of the college grounds, from the upper story of the library building to the Philosophical Hall on the opposite side, the ends terminating in two wells. Through this wire, signals were sent from time to time, from my house to my laboratory."

Upon the invention of the relay would rest the successful operation of the telephone and telegraph, but the modest professor had not yet learned the necessity of publishing his discoveries promptly. As a result, Sir Charles Wheatstone claimed the invention of the telegraph for Great Britain, and in the United States, Samuel F. B. Morse realized millions on his telegraph patent which was based on Henry's discoveries in electromagnetism. Both these men owed what they knew about the relay to Henry.

When the time came to settle questions of claim his students testified to his having demonstrated the relay principles in the classroom. And Henry, against his wishes, was forced to explain in a legal action how by opening the circuit of his large quantity magnet, loaded with hundreds of pounds of weight, ". . . the weights would fall, and great mechanical effects could thus be produced, such as the ringing of church bells at a distance of a hundred miles or more . . ."

Was it simply procrastination that caused him to delay

announcing his discovery? When urged by a friend to take out a patent for the application of his principle to the telegraph, he, like Franklin before him, refused to reap personal gain from a discovery which he believed belonged to everyone. To the despair of his friends, Henry went right on working, content to illustrate his experiments only to his worshipping students.

Early in his Princeton career Henry formed a friendship with two prominent Philadelphians. One of them was Professor Robert Hare, who taught chemistry at the Medical School of the University of Pennsylvania. Hare was the inventor of a large battery that generated intense heat; he was interested in all things electrical, and was delighted to find a kindred spirit in Henry. They met frequently to carry on electrical experiments together.

It is very likely that Henry met Professor Hare through Alexander Dallas Bache, great-grandson of Benjamin Franklin and Professor of Natural Philosophy at the University of Pennsylvania. A brilliant physicist, his interest was in terrestrial magnetism. In 1830 he had begun making observations in a small building attached to his house. His wife, Nancy and Harriet Henry also became fast friends, their friendship lasting as long as they lived.

Alexander Bache was in charge of research at the Franklin Institute and an active member of the American Philosophical Society. He prevailed upon Henry to give a series of lectures at the Society meetings.

The first lecture in the series on "Contributions to Electricity," given early in 1835, dealt with a crank-operated galvanic battery. (In a mural at the entrance of the Engineering Building in Princeton, painted over a century later, Henry's demonstration of this elaborate piece of apparatus is depicted in connection with electro-dynamic induction.)

While he had planned his paper to deal only with the description of this complicated battery, Henry added a few remarks off the cuff. These dealt with a new conductor—strips or ribbons of copper wire, nearly one-eighth of an inch wide, insulated with silk and coiled into a spiral like a watch-spring.

Several days later one of those coincidences, which seemed fated to be linked with Henry's discoveries, produced a wave of chagrin in the scientific community of Philadelphia. A copy of an English journal arrived in America, carrying an article by Michael Faraday describing as his original discovery the phenomenon of self-induction, the same process that Henry had reported more than two years earlier in Silliman's *Journal.*

This proved once more that Faraday, like so many other Europeans, paid little attention to the contributions of the American scientist. This time the irate Bache was determined that his dear friend should not be robbed of his rightful priority in announcing the intensifying effect of a long conductor wound into a spiral. Bache arranged for prompt publication of an abstract of Henry's talk in the *Journal of the Franklin Institute.*

Meanwhile, in his remarks at the Society lecture, Henry referred to his paper of 1832 and went on to explain how he had since then extended his studies of self-induction. Using a single pair (of plates) of his novel battery, he found, as before, that when the poles of a magnet were connected by a piece of copper bell-wire 5 inches long, no spark was produced either on making or breaking the circuit. With a 15-foot wire he obtained a feeble spark; adding sections of 15 feet at a time, he noted a greater effect, until when he had a wire 120 feet long he obtained a maximum spark.

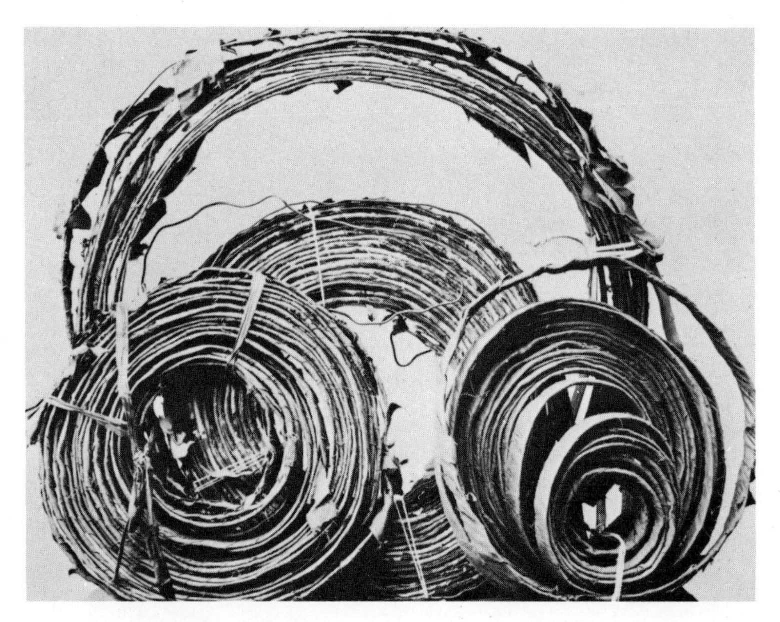

Helices insulated with silk

Thicker wire of the same length produced a greater effect, and a wire of 40 feet when coiled into a *helix* or spiral gave a more intense spark than the same wire uncoiled. When the copper ribbon was folded in the middle and folded again in a *flat* spiral there was no spark, thus showing that the induction of the current upon itself was neutralized by flowing equally in opposite directions in the double flattened spiral.

"The result was in accordance with the anticipation; the double spiral gave no spark whatever, while the other ribbon coiled into a single spiral produced as before a loud snap," wrote Henry about his discovery of non-inductive windings.

Two weeks after Henry's address in Philadelphia, Faraday read a paper before the Royal Society in London, describing non-inductive windings in almost the same words! Faraday and Henry—traveling along parallel paths in laboratories separated by a distance of three thousand miles, and by weeks or months in time of communication—were destined to meet.

By the end of his fourth year at Princeton, Professor Henry had already rendered outstanding service. He needed a rest, and the trustees of the College, showing both generosity of spirit and recognition of his worth, granted him a year's leave with full salary.

For the first time, Henry could afford to travel, and he grasped the opportunity to visit Europe. Harriet, tied down by three young children, could not go with him, but he would have as companion Richard DeWitt, the son of an old friend from the Albany Institute, who thought that the young man would profit by a close association with Professor Henry. An even happier circumstance was that Mr. Bache and his wife were also sailing for Europe, on a somewhat different mission.

Stephen Girard, a Philadelphia merchant, banker, and philanthropist, born in France, who had helped to finance the United States in the War of 1812, bequeathed money for the founding of Girard College. This was to be a free school for poor white orphan boys. Alexander Bache, appointed its first president, was going to Europe to study educational systems to prepare for his duties as the head of this unique institution.

Preparation for Henry's journey occupied three months, and included a trip to Washington to secure letters of introduction. It is not strange that his impressions of the capital were unfavorable, for Washington was a muddy, uncouth, overgrown village in those days. As for the architecture, he wrote Harriet, "it would scarcely be a loss were the British to again burn the Capitol—in that case I am sure, a more imposing and, at the same time, more simple building would be erected in its stead." He didn't like its "Italo-Romanesque" design, which he regarded as inferior to the Grecian style of architecture, and thought the pillars of the Corinthian order "too slender to appear well at a distance."

Except for John Calhoun, then Senator from South Carolina, whom Henry liked for his superior intelligence and interest in science, he had little to say about the other political leaders he met. He heard John Quincy Adams speak in Congress, and was cordially received by President-elect Martin Van Buren who arranged to get him letters of introduction to American ministers abroad.

Apparently, Henry felt that he would be short of funds for the European trip, which was to include purchase of electrical apparatus. In a letter to Erastus Corning, Mayor of Albany, he told of his itinerary—London, Paris, Edinburgh—and requested a loan of $900. "I will send Mr. DeWitt an order on you signed by my brother-in-law and myself and request Mr. DeWitt to give you a receipt for the money."

John Torrey wrote early in February that he had secured Henry passage on the *Wellington;* it was her first voyage, so that Henry should not be annoyed by bilge-water nor by creaking masts and joints, those irksome noises in stormy weather.

One other detail that Henry attended to was to pay an additional premium of $40 on his insurance policy of $4,000; across one side of the policy is a notation that Henry "has permission to proceed from hence to Europe . . ." and that in consideration of the extra payment his beneficiaries would be covered by insurance, should he be lost at sea.

To his sister Nancy, Joseph wrote that "Harriet will be lonely, but I hope she will soon become reconciled to my absence, and that she may pass pleasantly among her friends and relatives at the North. James informs me that you are much troubled about my sailing on account of the dangers of the voyage. It is not proper to make ourselves unhappy in anticipating troubles." Continuing in this vein, he reassures her about such dangers, since Providence protects us at sea no less than on land, and urges her not to worry when "contrary winds" blow.

A committee of three students at the college composed a letter in which they wished him a safe and profitable journey, saying: "On the occasion of your departure, we regret exceedingly, Sir, that we could not have remained longer under your instruction . . ."

On February 20, 1837, the voyagers set sail on the 750-ton packet which was scheduled to reach Portsmouth, England, within 18 days.

A few days later Harriet wrote to her brother-in-law James Henry: ". . . and now that he has gone and all things have been favourable I feel glad that he could go, and will endeavour to occupy both mind and body so that I may have no time to be gloomy." Would he tell Nancy that when it "may storm with us" it may be quite pleasant at sea. There is a great deal of comfort in believing that the sun shines on him while it may be almost "hidden from us."

The letter is full of homey details about the weather, Bub (Willie) doing well in school, and Mary talking endlessly about going to Albany, washing her face two and three times a day for the Albany relatives to kiss. ". . . our little pup has regained almost all the flesh she lost in her sickness . . ."; Louisa, Stephen's wife, is anxious to get home as early as she can. They all plan to spend the summer in Albany, but Harriet adds: "Aunty Platt is fond of children but I guess she will get enough of them when I come with all three."

CHAPTER *8*

Professor Abroad

AN EASTERLY WIND BUFFETED the *Wellington* off the English coast, so that it seemed they would never go up the English Channel. When the captain offered to put a boat ashore at Plymouth for those who had become restless, Henry and DeWitt were among those who accepted. For, as he wrote Harriet, "Our ship's company was very pleasant and we had every attention and luxury which could be desired, . . *but* I was very glad to escape from the dominion of Neptune and happy again to be on Terra Firma."

Besides wanting to plant his feet once more on solid earth, Henry was glad of the opportunity to visit Plymouth and to meet, at the Royal Dockyard, Sir William Snow Harris to whom he had a letter of introduction. "Mr. Harris is celebrated for his zeal in science and for his researches, particularly on the laws of electrical attraction and repulsion, made with new and ingenious instruments constructed by himself," he wrote Harriet.

Mr. Harris invited Henry to the kitchen where he was then engaged in experiments to determine the laws of induction. The next day he showed Henry around the town and the Dockyard, where they watched the making of immense ropes. Henry was very much impressed with the reeling machinery that mechanically wound the rope fiber on spools, and of which he made a diagram. The King's ropes were all marked by a red thread woven into the middle.

Going through every part of the works, he saw the making of masts and spars; a ship built of teak-wood awaiting coppering of its keel against shipworms, the forging of anchors on giant anvils, the metal being lifted by machinery and "suffering to fall on the anvil"; the valve-gates of the drydocks which admitted the largest ships and the steam engines that pumped out the water. In a field of special interest to Henry were Mr. Harris's hourly observations on temperature, rain gauges, and barometers.

The 75-acre shipyard was manned by 22,000 workers, some of whom were building a new breakwater, which he sketched in his diary. He purchased polished specimens of the stone used in its construction.

From Plymouth, Henry and DeWitt took the stage to London. They were scheduled to cross the stark and windy Salisbury Plain at night. Resolved not to miss the rough-hewn immense blocks and columns of Stonehenge, where the Druids were supposed to have worshiped, Henry tipped the driver to make a brief stop there. While the other passengers were huddled asleep in their seats, Henry walked under the light of a bright moon beside these ancient ruins that had defied the winds and rains for thousands of years. They left an unforgettable impression on him.

Arriving in London on March 17, 1837, he put up at a modest inn and the next day set out to find lodgings. He located at 37 Jermyn Street ". . . within a few steps of the Palace of St. James and about the same distance from the Royal Institution. I have often, as you may suppose, visited the latter, but do not intend to pay much court to the former," he wrote home.

As was proper, he next presented himself to the minister from Washington, with the letter of introduction from President Van Buren. This meeting obtained for him the emissary's help in reaching the people he wanted to see in London. Had it not been Easter vacation, Henry would have headed straight for the Royal Institution and the offices of the Royal Society. But as it was, he could in the meantime take a look around London, where he found the buildings "as black as if formed of cast iron," and the terraces, "as if powdered with a thick coat of lampblack . . ."

One of his letters of introduction led him to the home of a brother of Henry Vaughan whom he knew from the Franklin Institute. At dinner that evening he chanced upon Richard Rush, former minister to Great Britain, and son of the distinguished American physician, Benjamin Rush. The business that carried the younger Rush to London at this time was a decade or so later to figure prominently in Henry's life. Mr. Rush was representing the American government in the settlement of James Smithson's will which included the bequest for the founding of the Smithsonian Institution.

By this time Professor Bache and his wife had arrived, and so in the temporary absence of the man he wanted most to see—Michael Faraday—Henry toured London with his friends. He thought the inside of St. Paul's "magnificent," but remarked: "It is, however, a commentary upon the character of the last two centuries of this people that there are but three or four monuments to men of literature and science, while the walls are covered with monuments of military and naval heroes."

So also in Westminister Abbey, he found that only a small

corner was reserved for the poets, while "the hero of barbarous war lies in a marble tomb reaching in many cases almost to the vaulted roof . . ."

Then on to practical matters. The visit to London gave him the opportunity to buy apparatus. He began a round of trips to laboratories, inspecting their equipment, taking note of instrument makers, and then visiting these merchants to confer with them about getting duplicates to bring back to Princeton. He had already spent 800 dollars for his purchases when he learned, much to his dismay, from Stephen Alexander's letter that his allowance from the College for this purpose was only 500 dollars.

The London scientists received him warmly. He met William Sturgeon, Charles Wheatstone, and John Frederick Daniell, inventor of the simple battery. All accorded him the honors due a distinguished visitor. At breakfast with Sturgeon he exchanged information on magnetic experiments and showed his host a simple method of forming a battery. Together with the Baches he called on Professor Daniell and was introduced to Professor Boyle of King's College, London, where he taught materia medica. Wheatstone, then Professor of Experimental Philosophy in King's College, was busy developing his telegraph, and Henry had the pleasure of telling him about his own system of two electromagnetic circuits. Two months later Wheatstone secured a patent on his telegraph system including the combination of circuits introduced by Henry more than a year earlier.

In the evening, in the company of Mr. and Mrs. Bache, he attended a performance of *Macbeth,* which he enjoyed, but noted that he "did not experience as much pleasure as formerly in the amusement of the stage."

Finally, he had a chance to meet the star of them all—

Michael Faraday

Faraday. It came somewhat as a surprise to the American visitor that his English host held him in great esteem. A sign of his high regard was that he spared the time to talk with Henry more frequently and longer than was his custom. Unlike Henry, who kept an open door to his laboratory and gave freely of his time to students and visitors, Faraday maintained a strict rule of seeing no one for three days a week. Having no teaching or administrative duties, no children to make demands on his time, he could afford the luxury of seclusion in the best-equipped laboratory in Europe.

Yet despite Faraday's restrictive schedule, Henry managed to learn about his work and exchange ideas about common interests. When the Englishman invited him to lecture before the Royal Institution, Henry declined, saying that his purpose in coming to England was to learn and not to teach. He eagerly sat through Faraday's lectures on metals, a subject that he thought was the dullest in chemistry, but was most engagingly and instructively presented by Mr. Faraday.

Attending one of his popular lectures before an audience mostly of ladies, Henry wrote that: "Professor Faraday is deservedly a very popular lecturer, but does not surprise or strike one with the depth of his remarks, or the power of a profound mind, but moves by his vivacity of manner and his happy illustrations, as well as his inimitable tact in experimenting." Here the American showman at experimental demonstration gave his professional tribute to another master.

When her husband was unavailable to visitors, Mrs. Faraday entertained the American guest, taking him to visit people he was delighted to meet, and entertaining him with anecdotes of her husband's idiosyncracies. Henry was charmed with his delightful hostess.

The day came when the modest American professor unintentionally demonstrated his familiarity with matters electrical. The incident took place at King's College, in Wheatstone's laboratory. Present were Faraday, Daniell, Wheatstone, and Henry. The three Britishers were conducting an experiment trying to extract a spark from a current generated by a *thermocouple,* an instrument that converts heat directly into electrical current; with this instrument small amounts of heat are detected.

Each in turn tried his hand at achieving a spark by closing and opening an electrical circuit with a very feeble current—but without success. As they were about to abandon the idea as impractical, the visitor, who had been patiently watching the other "electricians" and listening to their arguments concerning the failure, offered to show them how to draw a spark.

Faraday, still arguing, but ready to take up what seemed to him a foolish challenge, stepped aside for Henry to take over. Making use of his discovery of self-induction, he wrapped a long wire around a piece of soft iron, and added the little coil to one of the leads. When he opened the circuit he drew the spark the others had failed to get.

Faraday, wild with excitement, jumped up, clapped his hands and shouted: "Hurrah for the Yankee experiment! Whatever did you do?"

In his quiet and patient manner, the man whose discovery of induction had gone unnoticed by the scientists, who had failed to read his paper, explained just what he had done. The "extra" voltage from self-induction of the long wire gave the added strength necessary to produce the visible sparks.

In a laboratory in King's College one can see displayed the two coils of copper ribbon insulated with silk that Henry used to demonstrate his experiment to the man who had already received world acclaim for his discovery of induction.

A few years after this incident Wheatstone and Faraday recommended to the Council of the Royal Society that Henry be awarded the Copley Medal, an honor that had been accorded only to Franklin. The Council deemed that it was not yet timely to place this laurel on the American. Somehow this postponed recognition never came.

In his meanderings in London some small satisfactions must have warmed Henry's heart, because he noted them in his diary. On a visit to the Adelaide Gallery he saw one of his own magnets displayed. While delivering a letter from Dr. Hare to one of the editors of the *Philosophical Magazine,* the latter "showed me an article in the Magazine on subjects

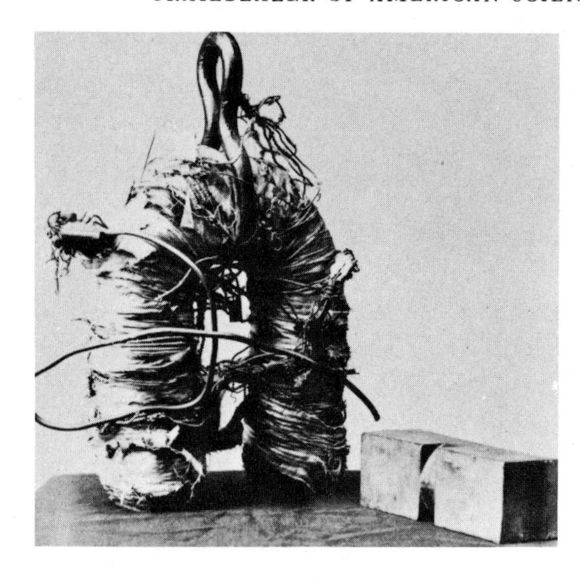

One of Henry's electromagnets

which had been settled by Henry in America," he jotted down.

His interest in every branch of science drew him to everything new in his path. He would make rough notes on the spot, and at leisure transcribe them to his "journal." Even the little commonplaces that often intrigued him he would write up in the minutest detail.

He wrote his wife a treatise on how to make tea as he had seen it done in England. It was necessary to heat the water to "real boiling." If it was difficult to get at the cover, he suggested that the end of a poker be placed against the kettle, and the other to the ear. "The sound conveyed by the iron will give, with great precision, the state of affairs within the vessel." The kettle had to have a high polish to retain the heat, and its bottom had to be blackened to absorb heat from the fire. He noted the exact amount of tea for each cup of water to produce "a very pleasant strength of decoction"; the hot water had to be poured on the tea and not the other way; the cup had to be rinsed with hot water to take off the chill, the sugar put in first, the cream added next for better taste, and after about half a minute the hot tea. "Some chemical action probably takes place between the sugar and cream before the addition of the tea." He gave a few further instructions on the importance of *China* tea cups, and of keeping sugar from getting into the saucer, because of "cohesion as a principle of science." He promised Harriet to discuss the making of coffee when he got home.

His letter added that when DeWitt first landed in England he was extremely anxious not to be recognized as an American. However "his ignorance of the Philosophy of tea making" betrayed him, much to his mortification.

After two months in England, visiting with the world's greatest physicists of the time, Henry reluctantly made the Channel crossing to France: "I feel much regret in parting from the kind friends I have made in this place," he remarked.

He arrived in Paris on May 10th and marveled at the strangeness and beauty of the French capital in spring. For two weeks he toured the city, taking note of sights unfamiliar to him: women sitting in groups on the sidewalks chatting and sewing, others working as clerks, managing shops, making watches and shoes, or sweeping the streets. Strange also was the sight of men harnessed to carts, drawing stone or goods, while others were engaged "in unproductive labor," exhibiting feats of strength, or picking up rags and bits of paper. "Some are thus engaged in the night and may be seen with a large basket on the back and a lantern in the hand, inspecting every pile of rubbish in their road."

Henry's Parisian visit coincided with the marriage of the King's son, the Duke of Orleans, which afforded him a glimpse of the ways of royalty. The King is seldom seen in public, he said, a policy designed to enhance his station in the eyes of his subjects. On occasions when the royal family was driven through the streets, they were surrounded by secretly armed police who gave each other signals as the royal carriage approached. This he thought must be a "sad drawback to their pleasures."

The royal wedding brought the multitudes into the streets. Called out by their cries, His Majesty appeared on the balcony of the palace fronting on the garden of the Tuilleries, and presented his new daughter-in-law to the throng. But there was little applause. "The Royal actor is far from being popular," Henry commented.

On one of several occasions when he visited the Luxembourg Galleries he saw the royal family and their attendants at close range, "a very ordinary collection of individuals." For Harriet's benefit he commented that "the great in circumstances are not always the favorites of Nature, either in mind or body."

Coming from a country with a small standing army made up of volunteers, he frowned upon the compulsory French service in the National Guard for all able males including professors! From the window of the Hotel·Normandie on the Rue Saint Honoré he watched with some amusement a military ceremony put on every morning for the benefit of a colonel, a guest in the same hotel. On Sunday, a review day, there was a grand display of 1,000 men parading with a band of music under the colonel's window.

"I should dislike the military system," was his pointed remark.

But interest in these sidelights was short-lived. By chance he met Thomas Hun, an old friend from Albany, who had

Henry in middle life

gone to France to study medicine and was living with other foreign students in the Latin Quarter. An American in Paris with a meager knowledge of the language, Henry was lost insofar as meeting and talking with scientists went. He immediately enlisted Hun as an interpreter, while at the same time brushing up on his French with the aid of a Parisian instructor.

The French scientists were as friendly and warm as the English, but the older men were too occupied with their teaching duties and, as members of the Chamber of Deputies, also with politics. They could spend little time with him, Henry complained. Still he managed to meet Guy Lussac, the celebrated chemist, and heard him lecture on the solidification of carbonic acid, which was most interesting despite "my imperfect understanding of the language." Yet from his detailed description of the process in his diary, he appearently missed very little. He also talked with De LaRive, the Swiss inventor of the electrical coil, who was then visiting Paris.

At the meeting of the Institut de France, he found its members inattentive, with their noses in their newspapers while the scientific papers were being read. Punctual and regular attendance was assured by imposing a fine on late or absent members.

Arrangements were made for Henry to see the methods of lighting the coast of France under the direction of Mr. Fresnel, the brother of the physicist who had devised the principle of the polygonal lens for lighthouses. Henry found the visit most instructive. He was interested in the lenses, prisms, and lanterns, and in the method of pumping oil into the lamps, although he had no notion at the time that some fifteen years later he would be called upon to introduce these very innovations into American lighthouses.

Henry left Paris in the middle of the summer, and made a two-day journey to Brussels, the Belgian capital, where he enjoyed several days of sightseeing. He noted the neatness of its houses and the prosperity and comfort of the people, which he attributed to the "more advanced state of its agriculture." Then he went on to Antwerp, where he was impressed with the similarity of the tall-gabled brick houses to those he had known in Albany which showed the stamp of the early Dutch settlers.

On his return to London he looked up his former student Henry James, who had withdrawn himself from all his friends and was living with a Negro servant. The warm-hearted professor did everything he could to take the crippled James away from his books and out of his unhealthy seclusion. Often he took James along when he visited acquaintances in London, but found himself embarrassed by the table talk on the subject of James's Negro slave. He was forced to put up a feeble defense with the argument that England had her own slaves in its colonial peoples.

Faraday entertained him again, and on one occasion took him to see the first section of the newly opened Birmingham railroad. Henry showed his boyish delight while riding on the locomotive, and was full of admiration for the engineering skill involved in the excavating of the two tunnels through which the train passed on its way to Birmingham.

The third and last lap of his European journey took him to Edinburgh, the capital of his ancestral Scotland. Especially because of his familiarity with Scottish history and folklore, he enjoyed the beauties of the ancient university city, and thought its architecture by far surpassed that of London, and even Paris.

During his pleasant visit there he met Sir David Brewster, founder of the British Association of Science, and inventor of a multiple lens for lighthouses. The Scottish scientist had shown his great admiration of Henry's work by including an account of it in his article on magnetism in a new edition of the *Encyclopedia Britannica.*

He was most cordial to Henry, and invited him to his home. There Henry had the special treat of seeing a letter in the handwriting of Sir Isaac Newton, and of examining the original manuscript of Newton's *Principia.* In the company of Lady Brewster he made a pilgrimage to Sir Walter Scott's Abbotsford. After enjoying the engaging hospitality of the Brewsters, he made a round of visits to his mother's relatives in Ayrshire.

He next visited Cambridge, where he met Professor John Steven Henslow, the botanist who had started Charles Darwin on his career as a naturalist, and who had spent much of the previous winter helping Darwin sort out the scientific treasures on the voyage of the *Beagle.* Henry was invited to spend a few days at Dr. Henslow's country manse. Then he went on to Liverpool, where he was invited to speak to the physics section of the British Association, giving a brief account of his researches with the Leyden jar.

Dropping in on a meeting on the Mechanics of Engineering, he was recognized by the chairman, who asked him to say a word or two about the progress of the steam engine in the United States. With pride in his country's achievements, Henry mentioned that the steamboat had been developed to the point where it could travel at fifteen knots. A skeptical listener charged him with the exaggeration typical of Americans, a remark that brought many to their feet in defense of the distinguished foreigner.

"They might as well talk of making a voyage from New York or Liverpool to the moon," the skeptical Englishman persisted.

Shortly afterwards Joseph Henry boarded the *Toronto,* and was on his way back from his eventful and instructive journey abroad. During the first half of the twenty-six-day crossing he was wretchedly seasick, which made him all the more eager to get home. A high spot of the voyage was his first acquaintance with St. Elmo's fire, a ball of light surrounding the mast of a ship in a storm. From a seasoned mariner on board, the scientist in electricity learned that this "faint light . . . of the phosphorescent kind," was the oldest known form of static electricity.

Though he was delighted to be home, Henry was full of enthusiasm for all he had learned abroad, and more eager than ever to continue with his investigations.

CHAPTER 9

Happy Years in Princeton

FOR MANY reasons the years at Princeton were golden ones for Henry. The quiet serenity of campus life suited him. He and Mrs. Henry made lasting friendships among their academic neighbors. He enjoyed his beautiful spacious home whose rooms rang with the laughter and chatter of his children. The lawn and walks of the campus in front of Nassau Hall were his front yard, shaded by the stately elm trees. And through the large windows he could gaze across to Philosophical Hall which housed his cherished coils, batteries, magnets, wires, and Leyden jars.

The well-spent year in Europe had been invigorating for Henry. This was shown by the elaborate and fertile experiments that followed during the next few years. And his contact with foreign scientists, who at last acknowledged his superior contributions, spurred him on to announce his discoveries. A steady stream of papers flowed from his pen to be published in the *Proceedings* of the American Philosophical Society.

In the spring of 1838 he announced to the Society that when a Leyden jar was discharged through a good conductor, a secondary shock—more intense than the primary shock directly from the jar—could be obtained from a perfectly insulated conductor nearby. Then, working straight through the summer vacation, he went on to demonstrate successive orders of induction through a series of coils—third, fourth, and fifth.

He prepared a number of flat coils of copper ribbon about 1½ inches wide, insulated with two layers of silk. Most of the coils contained 60 feet of copper, and one was 93 feet long. There were both *ribbon* coils and *wire* coils (helices). He wound each of these coils in such a way that one could be inserted inside the other. The total helix measured 9,000 feet, but by this arrangement, he combined the coils to give him different lengths at will. In the circuit there were also a small quantity magnet, and a set of Daniell cells for the source of the primary current.

By alternating the ribbon and wire coils, he established the fact "that an intensity current can induce one of quantity . . . and the converse . . . that a quantity current can induce one of intensity." Even when the battery power was small, the presence of the longer helices made it possible to obtain a current of great intensity when the circuit was opened.

Despite the rapid advances in electrical knowledge at this time, there was as yet no instrument to measure the *quantity* of current. Henry detected weak currents by placing the electrodes on his tongue, and stronger currents were felt by shocks through the hands. Describing his results with this experiment he said: "It was found that with the small battery a shock would be given from the current of the third order to twenty-five persons joining hands; also shocks perceptible in the arms were obtained from current of the fifth order."

Thus he used his pupils as shock detectors. This is not to say that the professor didn't shock himself many a time, but what better way was there to demonstrate his results to his students than by letting them *feel* his discoveries?

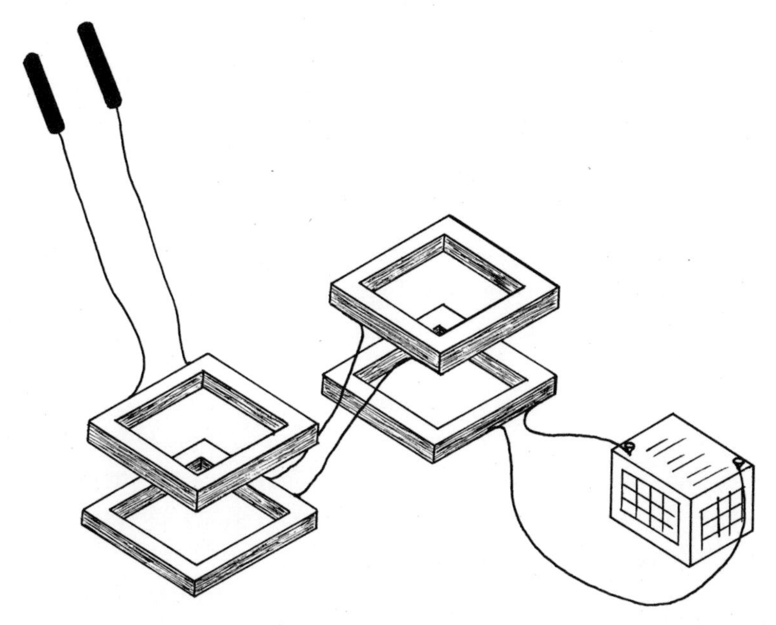

Diagram of Henry's transformer. Coil 1 is connected with the battery; a current is induced in coil 2; when this was connected with coil 3, a current was induced in coil 4. By holding a pair of electrodes (upper left) in his hands, Henry was able to gauge how much the coils stepped the voltage up or down

By means of a small magnetizing coil wound around a straw tube containing a sewing needle he found also these successive induced currents were alternating or "reversed to each other." The needle swung first in one direction, then in the opposite.

By varying these basic experiments in many ways he developed the principle of the modern transformer, which has its greatest use in long-distance transmission of electric power. In Henry's experiment the transformer consisted of a coil of flat copper stripping connected to a battery. When the current was interrupted, a current was induced in a second coil placed on top of the first and separated by a piece of glass to insure perfect insulation. As often as the current in the first circuit was broken, a powerful current was induced in the secondary one. But this shock could scarcely be felt above the fingers, he noted. In other words, while the quantity of current had been increased, its voltage had been "stepped down." When he substituted a longer coil in the second circuit, the magnetizing power was considerably reduced, but the shocks were more powerful. By holding a pair of electrodes leading from this circuit, he was able to *feel* how much the coils stepped up or stepped down the voltage.

The principle was somewhat analogous to alternately changing the water-flow and pressure in tubes by changing their length, diameter, and height.

The transformer principle is applied in today's powerhouse. Electricity from the dynamo is led into a step-up transformer, which increases its voltage and decreases its amperage several hundred times. On high-voltage or "high-tension" lines this current is carried to local sub-stations, where step-down transformers decrease the voltage, making safe the transmission of current along city streets.

Henry never failed to follow through to a conclusion any electrical phenomenon that excited his curiosity. It had been known since ancient times that the electric eel immobilized its prey by some strange discharge of energy. He pondered over the idea that the intense shock discharged from the electrical organs of the eel might be the effect of a secondary current, and he proceeded to construct an artificial eel.

He arranged a primary ribbon coil with a secondary coil from which extended two terminal handles. Both insulated coils were immersed in a shallow vessel of water, with the handles placed at the "two extremities of the diameter of the helix [secondary coil of wire]," and as he plunged his hands into the water, "parallel to a line joining the two poles," he felt a shock through the arms. And so the artificial eel, shocking the professor, reproduced the discharge from the electrical organs of a live eel.

Joseph Henry was first and foremost an experimenter. His genius lay in extracting scientific facts and discovering principles. He derived his principles from what philosophers call the inductive method, on which he lectured to his students.

From the lecture notebook of Henry C. Cameron, a cherished student at Princeton, we find that Henry taught that facts are gathered first by "simple observation." Thus, in astronomy, we learn that the moon revolves around the earth, because on one night it occupies a particular position next to a fixed star, and on the next night it has moved away from it. A second way is to experiment, "in which we bring about as it were, a new process of nature by placing matter in some unusual condition." If we wish to know what heat does to iron, we could put it in the fire and see that it melts. This would be an experiment, but "we might discover this observation, if we chanced to see a house burned down or melted iron thrown from a volcano."

Then, we discover principles or laws by the inductive process. In Cameron's notebook, it is the process "by which a general law is inferred from particular facts. This consists generally in making a number of suppositions as to the nature of the law to be discovered, and adopting the one which agrees with the facts." Then the law is verified by further testing it by experiment.

And finally, there is deduction—"the inverse of induction," which consists "in reasoning forward from a law which has been established by induction. Thus all the facts relative to the movements of the heavenly bodies have been derived by mathematical reasoning from the laws of motion and universal gravitation."

Henry's discovery that the discharge from a Leyden jar was *oscillatory*—not continuous, but vibrating, swinging back and forth—was a fact. That his "bobbin-wound" magnet would lift much heavier weights than Sturgeon's of the same size was a principle. The principle of the intensity circuit and relay

Receiving apparatus used in Henry's electromagnetic telegraph at Princeton

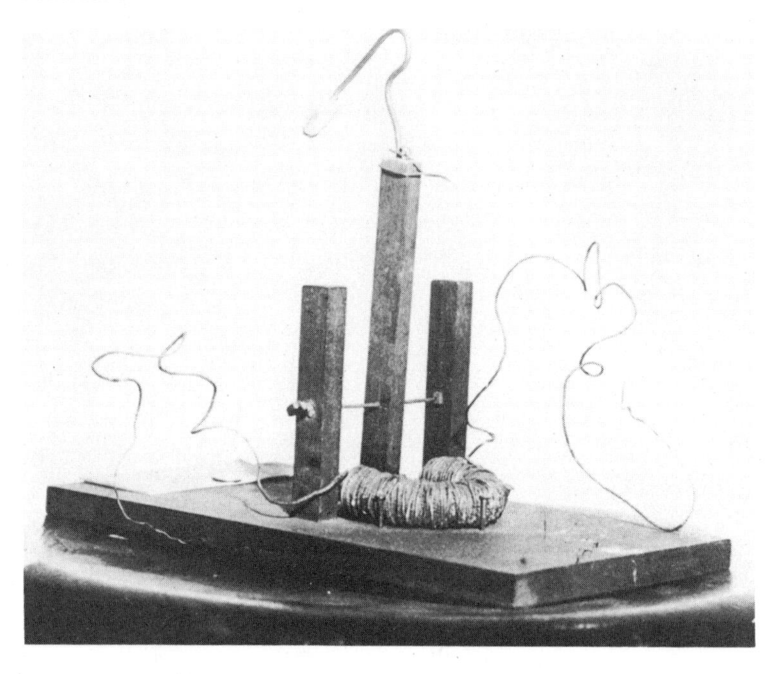

was the foundation on which Morse built his practical system of transmitting electric impulses over long distances.

Half a century before wireless waves were discovered, Henry obtained magnetic effects through space as far as 220 feet from the sparks. In 1842 he reported: "As these are the results of currents in alternate directions, they must produce in surrounding space a series of plus and minus motions analogous to if not identical with undulations [*waves*]." Leaving the development of both practical inventions and sweeping theories to others, Henry continued his experiments in Philosophical Hall.

Among these was the demonstration that every spark of electricity set off from his electrical machine in Philosophical Hall produced electrical effects throughout the whole village. From the classroom notes of another of his Princeton students we learn that he considered that "A fact no more improbable than that light from a candle (probably another kind of wave or vibration . . .) should produce a sensible effect of the eye at the same distance."

Further pursuing this idea that electricity pervades all space, he connected a wire to the metal roof of his study, and carried the wire through a magnetizing spiral to the ground, and then to a series of needles in his study. With every flash of lightning within a radius of twenty miles of Princeton, the needles in his study were magnetized by the induced current developed in his wire.

Or, spark coils operating on the second floor of his laboratory building magnetized needles in the basement. The induction took place through 30 feet of air and two layers of 14-inch flooring. "It would appear that the transfer of a single spark is sufficient to disturb perceptibly the electricity of space throughout at least a cube of 400,000 feet of capacity," he wrote. On other occasions, putting on a show for friends or students, he would give them a shock when they held the wire ends of the coil being operated in the adjoining room.

From his explanation of this phenomenon it is clear that he had made a studied guess that electricity spreads by wave motion in a manner identical with the propagation of light. The proof of this came forty years later when Heinrich Hertz demonstrated the existence of radio waves, on which radio, television, and wireless communication are based.

Henry's major contribution was in the field of electromagnetism, but he gradually reached out into other fields. Learning of Becquerel's work in France, he repeated his experiments with phosphorescent substances—those which shine in the dark with a cold light. This had nothing to do with ordinary light emanating from great heat. In this field he discovered forty previously unknown phosphorescent substances.

In his accustomed manner of bringing a point home to his students in a way they could not forget, he would demonstrate phosphorescence during a bright aurora (Northern lights). On a sheet of paper he wrote letters or figures with quinine bisulphite. These were invisible by daylight or lamplight, but in the presence of the eerie light from the northern sky, they would glow distinctly with a pale blue light. This indicated the electrical nature of the aurora borealis.

Together with Stephen Alexander, he undertook to study the heat of different parts of the sun—especially the sunspots. Using a four-inch telescope they threw an image of the sun on a screen in a dark room. Through a hole in the screen they projected a sensitive thermopile which was connected with a galvanometer. By moving the telescope slightly, different parts of the sun's image were thrown on the thermopile. The metal in the thermopile being variously heated produced

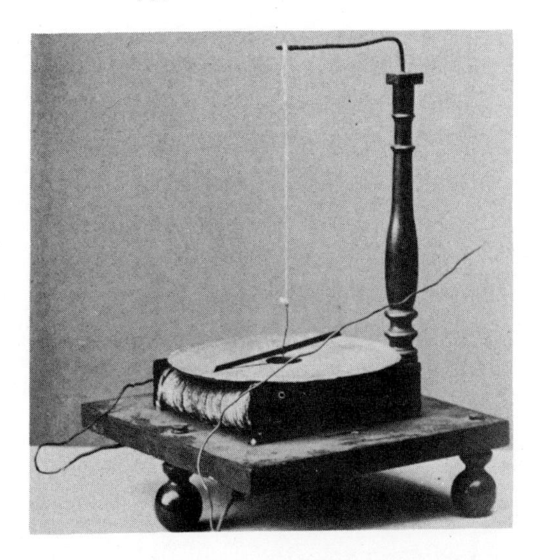

Galvanometer used by Joseph Henry

greater or less shift in the galvanometer needle. In this way they showed that all parts of the sun's surface did not give off an equal amount of heat, and that the sunspots radiated less heat than the surrounding areas.

The Princeton professor never missed a trick if it was at all possible to illustrate a principle by an unforgettable demonstration. Lecturing on sound, he ran a 30-foot pole from the basement to the attic of Philosophical Hall. At the top of it he hooked up "a rude imitation of a fiddle," while at the other end of the pole his servant Sam had attached a real fiddle. When Professor Henry gave a signal by ringing a bell, Sam would draw the bow across the fiddle in the cellar, playing some pre-arranged tune. Then the professor would gleefully explain to his students a principle in sound conduction and resonance as they listened to the weird sounds emanating from the sham fiddle near the ceiling.

In the summer of 1844, our professor spent a good part of his vacation blowing soap bubbles. He was studying the tenacity of soap film. By weighing the quantity of water that adhered to it before it burst, he measured the tensile (stretching) strength of the bubble. He showed that this power of a soap bubble to resist bursting was due not to increased molecular attraction, but to reduced mobility of the molecules. He also discovered that the cohesion of clear water was greater than that of soapy water.

Pursuing these experiments further he came to some conclusions about the cohesion of solids and liquids that upset the views then taught in the standard texts. Until then it was thought that solidity was distinguished from "liquidity" by the adhesion of the particles to each other in a solid. Henry disagreed. "The resistance of ice to extension or compression is found by experiment to differ very little from that of the water contained in a vessel," he wrote. The change from the solid to the liquid state was caused not by destruction of cohesion, but by the neutralization of the "polarity of the molecules" in such a way as to make them move freely "around every imaginable axis."

He never permitted any chance observation to go unexplored. One day a small lead tube about eight inches long happened to have been left with the bent end in a shallow dish of mercury. A few days later he noticed that the mercury had disappeared from the dish, and was spread on the shelf at the other end of the lead tube. Cutting through the tube, he discovered that the mercury had not "leaked" through the opening, but had percolated through the solid substance. To test this he used a solid rod of lead bent so that one end was immersed in the mercury, while the other end was placed in an empty dish. After 24 hours, a globule of mercury was found at the lower end of the lead rod, and after five days all the mercury passed through the solid rod into the dish.

In this way he discovered the unheard-of phenomenon that by capillary attraction one metal had "dissolved" another.

A manufacturer of bronze ornaments in Philadelphia was engaged in silver plating of copper, and Henry asked his co-operation in an experiment. He heated a piece of copper plated with silver to the melting point of the silver. The silver disappeared, but the workmen were not surprised. They had seen it happen before! "It burned off," they said. But Henry was not satisfied with this explanation. When the copper rod cooled, he dipped it into a solution that dissolved the end of the copper; as he had expected, the silver was again exposed, having penetrated a short distance into the copper.

Though, as we have demonstrated, Henry's first love was experimentation, he also loved to share his knowledge with his students, who worshiped him. He was popular for his exciting lectures, respected for his wisdom, knowledge, and lofty principles, and loved for his warm personal interest in every one of them. Years after they left his classes they could count on his advice and encouragement about a career, help in getting a position, wise direction when they were at the point of making an important decision.

To one young graduate he wrote about his chosen profession:

> I presume you are making good progress in your study of the law and I have little doubt that you will play a respectable part in the drama of active life. Besides knowledge and skill in your profession, aim at *discovering* a character for candor, honesty, and truth. Strive to be *worthy* of the confidence and patronage of the Public, and you will ultimately secure them.

Ending on a note of encouragement, he wrote: "Do not be discouraged should your rise be not as rapid as you expect. The tree of slowest growth strikes the deepest root."

Writing recommendations has always been part of a professor's chores, but Henry regarded it as a deep obligation which he discharged with warm sincerity. In turn, from many of his students he earned lifelong glowing affection. One of them wrote about him with reverence: "I always feel as if I were in the presence of a superior being. . . . May a star ever shine on the head of Nassau's nobleman—the great and wise Henry."

Henry had very definite ideas about the role of education which he said was "produced by coercion—at the expense of labor on the part of the educator, and of toil and effort on the part of the instructed." Critical of methods of instruction, he wrote in nearly modern terms:

> In this country, so far as I have observed, the course of education is defective in two extremes: it is defective in not imparting the mental habits of facilities which can most easily be acquired in early life, and it is equally defective in the other extreme, in not instructing the student, at the proper period, in processes of logical thought. . . . The value of facts, rather than of principles, is inculcated. The one however is almost a consequence of the other. If proper seeds are not sown, a valuable harvest cannot be reaped.

Nor did he neglect to point out the responsibilities of the administrators of an educational institution. Replying to a letter from Rev. Bullions, an instructor at the Albany Academy, he said: "I deeply sympathize with you in reference to the affairs of the Academy and do not agree with the trustees in opinion that your salary should be cut because your department does not pay its way."

Elaborating on the principle that the reputation of a scholar has enormous value for the college as a whole, the institution, and the city, he is sharply critical of the shortsightedness of the trustees.

Quite early in his association with the College he had become sufficiently involved in its financial affairs to write to the Hon. Stephen Van Rensselaer about a fund of $100,000 that was being raised from alumni: "Nassau Hall has peculiar claims on your kind regard," he wrote his patron of earlier years. "You have been one of her pupils and know that she has educated a large proportion of the men who have directed the affairs of the general government since its first establishment."

Henry's *Syllabus of Lectures at Princeton* shows that he had begun to make observations on types of energy that he divided into two classes: those which come from "celestial disturbance"—the powers of water, wind, and tide—and those derived from combustion—steam, heat, and "animal powers." Henry was beginning to see the interrelationship between different forms of energy. Had he continued his investigations, he might have approached one of the most fundamental laws of nature—the transformation and conservation of energy.

This was not to be, for at the end of 1846 an event of great moment in the history of scientific advancement proved to be another important turning point in the life and work of Joseph Henry.

Princeton was where he did much of his productive work, where his son received his education, and where he had achieved renown as the country's leading scientist. Here he had enormously enriched the science of physics, given brilliant leadership to the younger men and left a giant imprint on the path of knowledge. Here he gave "his heart and soul to the duties of the school."

No wonder that for years afterward he returned to give lectures, renew fond associations, and bask in the academic atmosphere. No wonder, too, that the University tried to get him back, but Henry's strong sense of duty called him to serve elsewhere.

The Joseph Henry House and Stanhope Hall, Princeton, in 1863

CHAPTER 10

Birth of the Smithsonian

In 1837, when Joseph Henry met him in London, the Honorable Richard Rush was representing the government of the United States in an amicable suit, and was making the legal arrangements for the transference of a strange legacy. The story of the bequest by an English gentleman who had died eight years earlier was more like a bit of romantic fiction than a true tale of an heirless scientist leaving his fortune to science.

James Smithson, born in 1765, was the illegitimate son of the first Duke of Northumberland and Elizabeth Macie, a descendant of King Henry VII, and one of the richest heiresses in England. James's half brother, General Earl Percy, led the British troops back from the Battle of Concord and Lexington, and on his return to England advocated freedom for the American colonies.

James grew up proud of his royal blood, but bitterly resentful of his father the Duke, who disowned him. At seventeen, James entered Oxford University, and when he graduated in 1786, he was reputed to know more than any one at the University about the chemistry of minerals. A year later, on the recommendation of Henry Cavendish, the man who identified hydrogen as an element, he was elected a Fellow of the Royal Society. Smithson published a number of papers in scientific journals, and read several before the Society. Among his intimate friends he counted not only the recluse Cavendish, but William Wollaston, the discoverer of paladium, and Dominique Arago, the French physicist. Smithson himself identified zinc carbonate, a mineral that bears his name—smithsonite.

Because of his illegitimacy, British nobility snubbed him, and Smithson, bearing a life-long grudge, left England and went to live in France. His fashionable home in the Rue Montmartre in Paris was a meeting place of prominent people, including visitors from America. He never visited the United States.

Smithson was consumed with a rankling hate against the British nobility to which he felt he rightly belonged. Particularly, he was determined to become more famous than the father who had rejected him. He said: "My name shall live in the memory of man when the titles of the Northumberlands and the Percys are extinct and forgotten."

He was not distinguished enough as a chemist to achieve fame—another reason for his bitterness. Despite the fashionable company he kept, he was a lonely man. He never married, and his only pastime was gambling. A shrewd enough mathematician, he recognized that a gambler's chance to win is slim, so he rationed the number of gold pieces he threw away at the European casinos, and managed to save enough of his inheritance from his mother to become, for those days, a man of great wealth.

There are only guesses as to why he chose, at the age of sixty, to make the United States the beneficiary of his great fortune. It is thought that at first he meant to leave his money to the Royal Society, but in a fit of anger because a paper

Left: James Smithson at 21, as an Oxford student; *Right*: Smithson at 51

of his was rejected, scratched that body off his list. Since he was accepted in France, he could have made his bequest to the French Academy, but possibly rejected that idea because, as a benefactor of that venerable society, he would have been only one of many.

His decision to leave his fortune to a country he hardly knew may have been partly influenced by an American visitor. Joel Barlow, the Revolutionary patriot, poet (a "Hartford Wit"), and Minister to France in 1811, may have impressed Smithson with the future greatness of a vigorous young nation. Perhaps leaving his fortune to a new country where science was only in its infancy appealed to him as a surer way to perpetuate his name.

Smithson died in 1829, leaving an annuity to his servant, and to his nephew the whole of the income from his property for life. He provided in his will that if the nephew died without heirs, the entire fortune would go "to the United States of America, to found, at Washington, under the name of the Smithsonian Institution, an establishment for the increase and diffusion of knowledge among men."

Six years later Smithson's nephew died, leaving no children.

When President Andrew Jackson announced to Congress that it had become the guardian of the estate of an English gentleman, the question was raised as to whether the bequest should be accepted. Among those who fought against accepting money from a foreigner was John Calhoun, an avowed foe of Jackson, and a staunch defender of states' rights. Congress had no authority to receive a personal gift, he declared. Others in the Senate argued that there was no precedent, as if such happenings were likely to have precedents!

However, there were those who spoke eloquently for acceptance: Senator Rufus Choate, a famous orator, Robert Dale Owen, son of the famous social reformer, and John Quincy Adams, the wise old statesman. Finally, the matter was settled with the decision to accept the legacy of 105,960 pounds sterling—half a million dollars.

In 1838, Richard Rush arrived in New York with 105 bags, each containing 1,000 gold sovereigns, and another 960 sovereigns and "eight shillings and sevenpence wrapped in paper." Then followed eight years of wrangling in Congress as to how the bequest should be used. Smithson had set forth in his will that it be used "for the increase and diffusion of knowledge among men." But all kinds of interpretations were placed upon the meaning of these nine words.

The very Congressmen who had opposed acceptance of

the gift as unconstitutional or beneath the dignity of the government now proposed all manner of schemes for its disposal. One wanted to establish a great astronomical observatory, another pleaded for an agricultural school, others argued for a library, a national university, a museum, a school for women. Colleges wanted a share of the fund, societies sought to get a portion to defray the cost of their meetings and printing of transactions, and still others called for an agricultural bureau. In session after session politicians argued, each for his own pet scheme or political advantage.

It was John Quincy Adams who pleaded that the fund be snatched "as from a rattlesnake's fangs" from the "mountebank projectors and shallow and worthless pretenders to science." After years of debate Adams framed an Act which was passed by Congress in 1846, establishing the Smithsonian Institution. On August 10th of that year, President James Polk signed the law by which the Smithson fortune was lent to the United States Treasury. The government agreed to pay six per cent interest on the fund in perpetuity, the relationship of the Government to the Institution to be that of guardian to ward. The preamble of the law stated that Congress provided "for the faithful execution of said trust agreeable to the will of the liberal and enlightened donor."

Congress further provided that the President and the members of his Cabinet should be members of the Institution, but that it be governed by a Board of Regents, composed of the Vice-President and the Chief Justice of the United States, three Congressmen, and six citizen members. The Board of Regents was to choose a suitable person as Secretary of the Institution, to be its administrative officer.

The law called for the erection of a building of plain but durable construction to receive objects of natural history, to contain a chemical laboratory, a library, an art gallery, lecture rooms, and offices for the staff. The secretary would have charge of the building, museum, library, and all of the property of the Institution, and would employ the necessary assistants.

Once the Board of Regents was created and appointments made, a committee that included Robert Dale Owen, Rufus Choate, and Professor A. D. Bache, got to work to plan the organization. The Board's first act was to consult the foremost American scientist about a plan of aims and objectives. How did Professor Henry think the Institution should be run? Would Mr. Henry study the will, and present a plan for operation?

Henry had undoubtedly followed the long debate about the disposal of the Smithson legacy, and had formed some ideas about the project. He must have been guided first by what he thought was the benefactor's wishes, and second by the limits of the fund. While half a million dollars was, for that time, a great sum, he knew that it could be easily dissipated by too grandiose a plan. Discretion was demanded if the fund was to remain intact and only the income spent.

He entitled the document embodying his plan "An Institution for the Increase and Diffusion of Knowledge Among Men." By repeating the very words of the will, he asserted the intention of keeping faith with the donor. Since Smithson had a bent for scientific knowledge, the Institution was honor-bound to favor the sciences as against the arts, languages, or philosophy. To *increase* knowledge meant that part of the income would have to go for original research. He therefore proposed that able scientists be encouraged to conduct investigation into new fields. To *diffuse* knowledge required the publication of papers, reports, and findings in all branches of science, and their wide distribution to all readers who could use them. The broader dissemination of scientific knowledge would include the translation of scientific information for and from other countries.

In the spirit of the donor Henry proposed that the benefits derived from the Institution should extend far beyond Washington or even the nation, and embrace all mankind. In this way, Henry also expressed the idea that science was international, and its fruits belonged to all the people.

Henry's plan did not please the politicians who favored local and provincial utilization of the fund, nor did it have popular appeal. It did, however, receive the support of the Board of Regents, who recognized its sober practicality as well as its broad vision. Henry's plan was accepted as a sensible means of achieving the most benefit from a modest income.

The next job before the Board was to find a Secretary "combining . . . the qualifications of a professor of the highest standing in some branch of science" with "efficiency as an executive officer and a knowledge of the world . . ." They were looking for a "representative of the Smithsonian Institution, to reflect honor on the office, not requiring to borrow distinction from it."

Who else but Joseph Henry could fill the post?

Alexander Bache, himself an influential scientist and educator, seeing great things to come from the new Institution, approached Henry in a letter to Princeton:

> *Come you must* for your country's sake. . . . You have a name which must go down to history as the great founder of a great institute. The first Secretary of *the* American Institute. Science triumphs in you, my dear friend, and come you *must.* Redeem Washington. Save this great national institution from the charlatans. Glori-

Alexander Dallas Bache

> ous results. In the midst of personal troubles, I forget all but that this great beginning stamps our Institution.

Joseph Henry was faced with a momentous decision. Should he forever turn his back on active research in the laboratory? He remembered that Newton made no discoveries after he accepted a position as warden of the British Mint. Should he leave behind his beloved Princeton, its students and faculty?

Ought he exchange the quiet of campus life for a post around which conflict of opinion had already raged for years? Who could guarantee that he would not become embroiled in controversy?

Henry desired neither riches nor the glory of public life. Yet he saw it as a public duty to give American science the needed impetus to growth. So when the Board of Regents unanimously extended the invitation, he accepted the position, exchanging, as he said to a friend, "future fame for present reputation."

On December 3, 1846, his appointment was announced. It received the warm approbation of scientists in this country and abroad. Hare, Silliman, Arago, Faraday, Sir David Brewster, and many others, applauded. Brewster, his distinguished host in 1837 now said: ". . . the mantle of Franklin has descended upon the shoulders of young Henry."

The *National Intelligencer* echoed: ". . . Foremost among American savants stands the name of Franklin, a name which belongs to the world. Secondly, perhaps to Franklin only, stands the name of the philosopher of Princeton. If Franklin discovered the identity between lightning and electricity, Henry has gone further, and reduced electric and magnetic action to the same laws. . . .

"It is the man who gives dignity to the office, not the office to the man."

The appointment came as a surprise to Princeton. Reluctantly the college authorities released him, wished him good luck, and assured him that should he ever wish to return, he would be welcomed back.

Showing that he was well aware of the grave responsibilities he had assumed, Henry replied to the congratulatory message from President Nott of Union College: "The office is one which

I have by no means coveted and which I accepted at the earnest solicitation of some friends of science in our country, to prevent its falling into worse hands, and with the hope of saving the noble bequest of Smithson from being squandered on chimerical or unworthy projects."

Henry's credo that the "special knowledge of *each*" should become "the knowledge of *all*," found its fullest fruition in the organization of the Smithsonian. What Mark Twain called "that poor . . . mildewed old fossil," and the newspapers the "nation's attic" today's Secretary prefers to designate as the "conservator of America's cultural heritage." But Henry sought still other means of spreading knowledge.

Men of science, meeting in groups, had established innumerable small societies to report their work and exchange ideas. Henry recognized that much could be gained from channeling such information from local groups into one national organization, which would also cut down the waste of duplication. Even before he came to Washington, Henry had advocated a great national society of scientists, modeled after the British Association for the Advancement of Science.

Naturally, therefore, he was a prime mover in the discussions and plans in 1847 for an organization to embrace all the sciences. In 1848, the American Association for the Advancement of Science was founded, living evidence that American science had attained a degree of maturity. Henry was elected president of the Association the next year, showing the high esteem in which he was held by scientists in every field.

CHAPTER 11

The Smithsonian Flourishes

HENRY's first disappointment came with the plans for an elaborate building to house the Institution. James Renwick Jr., the architect who had designed Grace Church and later also St. Patrick's Cathedral in New York, was engaged to lay the plans. The Norman castle he designed was not in keeping with Henry's simple taste or his sense of frugality. However impressive an ornament to the capital, it was a "Romanesque" structure of a "pile of bricks and mortar," with useless towers.

The cornerstone was laid on May 1, 1847 with all the pomp of gun salutes, brass bands, and political speeches. The site chosen on the Mall was called the "Island," because it was cut off from the rest of the city by a dirty canal, an inland waterway between the Potomac and the Eastern Branch, which has since been filled in. Construction of the building proceeded slowly. Even after it was completed, wooden planks, laid across the muddy, unkempt waste that surrounded it, had to be crossed to reach its lecture halls.

Almost from the beginning Henry encountered opposition. The Act of Congress called for a museum to display geological and mineralogical exhibits, a library, an art gallery, a chemical laboratory, and lecture rooms. Henry didn't regard a huge book collection and costly paintings as a way of either increasing or diffusing knowledge. He ran into difficulty with the naturalists who wanted an accumulation of specimens, while his plan was to offer materials that would extend information about them.

What kind of printed materials should be issued by the Institution? Here Henry came into conflict with the man in

Looking southeast towards Smithsonian Institution. Note the canal in front of the building and the rest of Washington in the foreground of the picture

the street. Henry saw no need to publish popular magazines or elementary textbooks, which could well be left to private publishers. Instead, he envisioned the publication of rare works, learned documents, scientific treatises which were neglected by commercial publishers because of the high costs of production and small printings. The first publication that he announced was the archaeological work of Squier and Davis, *The Ancient Monuments of the Mississippi Valley,* which dealt with the prehistoric Indian remains of the Ohio and Mississippi valleys.

He established two types of publications: *Smithsonian Contributions to Knowledge* and *Smithsonian Miscellaneous Collections,* volumes that contained original scientific contributions, elaborately illustrated descriptions of species of plants, animals, and geological formations, physical tables, reports of expeditions, and research findings. While of little interest to the general reader, these represented valuable sources for scholars all over the world. These works he personally edited for clarity, accuracy, and precise wording.

In addition, the Secretary's annual reports carried accounts of progress in every branch of knowledge, translations of classic papers by the world's leading scientists, and transactions of learned societies. In his selection, Henry never gave more than its due to his own field of investigation. Published promptly, the contributions in all fields were made available to the workers in those fields without protection by copyright—free to anyone who could use them. To this day such materials from the Smithsonian Institution can be reproduced without restricting copyright laws.

Next Henry organized a system of international exchange of publications. The archives today are full of routine letters often written in his own hand arranging with Adams Express and the U. S. Custom House to distribute reading matter, minerals, "philosophical instruments," Indian relics, and lithographic stones throughout the world. As a result of his efforts, several steamship companies aided the exchange system by transporting packages without charge, and arrangements were made for transport duty-free. Shipments came and went to and from Bremen, Valparaiso, Hamburg, Liverpool, Zurich, Leipzig, Havana, Alaska, and other parts of the world.

Henry was proud of the exchange system, as he indicated in the Smithsonian Report of 1852:

> The worth and importance of the Institution are not to be estimated by what it accumulates within the walls of its building, but by what it sends forth to the world. Its great mission is to facilitate the use of all the implements of research, and to diffuse knowledge this use may develop. The Smithsonian publications are sent to some institutions abroad, and to the great majority of those at home, without any return except, in some cases, that of cooperation in meteorological and other observations.

On August 1, 1855, in a letter to the Hon. James Buchanan, Minister to England, Henry wrote: "The affairs of the Institution are in a flourishing condition, and we think much is accomplished through its instrumentality for the increase and diffusion of knowledge among men."

With the letter, went 33 boxes containing 8,585 parcels weighing 10,481 pounds.

Henry's early interest in meteorology was reawakened by the need for information about coastal and continental storms. Little was known of the methods of forecasting storms, and few facilities existed for transmitting information about on-the-spot observations of approaching weather changes. Henry urged

Receiving room, International Exchange Service, Smithsonian Institution, 1914

the Board of Regents to undertake the assembling of an organization of weather observers, a proposal he made only after informing himself about the feasibility of the project.

Among Henry's friends was James P. Espy, a meteorologist who developed a theory of storm formation. This pioneer weather man was known as "the Storm King." Then there was James H. Coffin, the first to point out that there were three important wind zones in the northern hemisphere; and William Ferrel, who later discovered that land winds and ocean currents are affected by the rotation of the earth.

Shortly after Arnold Guyot, the Swiss glacier expert, arrived in the United States, Henry met him at a meeting of the American Association for the Advancement of Science. He consulted the Swiss scientist about a project he had already discussed with Espy and others. Together they worked out a way to make observations of barometric pressure, temperature, humidity, wind velocity, and cloud formation simultaneously at different posts. The venture was modest enough, and Henry proposed to the Regents that they appropriate $1,000 for instruments to distribute to volunteer weather watchers.This small appropriation went a long way, because Henry persuaded Guyot to make the instruments, thus insuring also their uniformity and therefore greater accuracy of the observations.

The novel feature in this weather information system came from Henry himself. The Morse telegraph was by then in use. Henry proposed that the corps of volunteers transmit their reports telegraphically. Where previously there had been no way to anticipate the arrival of a storm from a distant storm center, it now became possible to be forewarned days before it broke. As the daily reports were received at the Institution, they were plotted on a large wall map with movable stick pins—the first daily weather map, inaugurated by Henry in 1849!

We can imagine Henry standing before the map explaining to friends and visitors at the Smithsonian, as the telegraphic reports flowed in: "This is the way we can predict when an approaching storm that started in Missouri will hit the Washington meridian." The visitor had only to wait to see that he forecasted accurately.

At first the weather observations came from a spot just west of the Mississippi. The next year while he was attending a meeting in Boston, Henry thought of a way by which the observations could be extended to take in a wider area. From Boston he went to Canada. In Toronto he went to see Captain J. Henry Lefroy at the Observatory, to enlist his support in widening the weather-reporting system. Then Henry returned to the United States to urge his own government to join in the weather exchange project. Soon there were observers in

Canada, Bermuda, the West Indies, and Central America, adding their information to that which was gathered from along the seacoast and the Great Lakes.

Henry, the chief weather forecaster, earned the nickname "Old Probabilities"; later his "probabilities" became weather "indications," and finally, as these observations became meaningful meteorological facts, the predictions proved reliable enough to be called "forecasts."

Henry, the scientist, was always interested in the underlying laws that explained natural phenomena; at the same time he was quick to see that such knowledge could serve practical purposes. "All knowledge is useful. . . . The discovery of today, which appears unconnected with any useful process, may in the course of a few years, become the fruitful source of a thousand inventions . . ." he wrote in one of his annual reports.

Advance weather information was as important to farmers as it was to shippers. Beginning in 1851, the weather observers were asked to report also on the migration of birds, the flowering and fruiting of plants, the hibernation habits of animals, the movements of fish, and on the opening and closing of harbors as ice formed and melted.

Reports of these observations were collected over a period of six years and then tabulated and published by the Smithsonian Institution. Henry wrote a series of articles in which he interpreted these findings. Published as *Meteorology in Its Connection with Agriculture,* the report dealt with atmospheric conditions, air movements and currents, land temperatures, and atmospheric electricity.

Introducing the subject so near to his heart, Henry wrote: "Independently of the practical value of knowledge of the principles on which the art of agriculture depends, the mind of the farmer should be cultivated as well as his fields, and . . . what is better fitted to improve the intellect than the investigation of the mode by which he produces the changes in the material universe?"

With the years, Henry's crew of observers grew to six hundred, and their work extended to the providing of information about local rock formation, types of terrain, archeological findings, and varieties of plants and animal life.

Near the end of the Civil War, Henry started to work toward the establishment of a national weather bureau that would take up the work that the limited funds of the Institution could not adequately sustain. Several years later this idea bore

One of Joseph Henry's offices in the Smithsonian Institution, probably in early 1860's

fruit. In 1870, regular weather bulletins were issued from the Cincinnati Observatory based on telegraphic messages from surrounding regions. About the same time Congress made provision for a national system organized by the Chief Signal Officer of the Army.

The new organization received all the help the Institution could provide, and when this new department outgrew its infancy, Henry was only too glad to turn over to it all the practical affairs of weather watching. His practice was to stimulate and nurture each new venture up to the time when it could stand on its own feet. Opposed to duplication of services, he was always ready to surrender his control of any department as soon as a government bureau undertook its sponsorship.

Henry made a point of surrounding himself with distinguished men in fields in which he himself was not expert, and of encouraging them with grants of assistance in their specialties. Spencer Fullerton Baird, a prominent naturalist, who was elected Assistant Secretary of the Institution, began first the study of birds and wild life, and later of food fishes in the coastal waters. This was the small beginning of what much later became the United States Bureau of Fisheries concerned with the conservation of fish resources.

Then came a number of exploratory expeditions into little-known parts of the United States and other parts of the world. Captain Charles Hall made two expeditions to the Arctic, which, following instructions prepared by Henry, added much to the geological information about this region. The purchase of Alaska from Russia in 1867 was made largely because of Spencer Baird's testimony about Alaskan wealth in minerals, timber, and other resources.

As the United States extended its frontiers and the West

was developed, scientists accompanied exploratory expeditions to all territories where telegraph wires were strung and steel rails laid. The geological study of the Colorado canyons, the surveys of the Mississippi Delta and of the Ohio River were the scientific by-products of these explorations, aimed at solving the practical problems of communication, flood control, and navigation. The geography and geology of the Utah range, since named the Henry Mountains, became known largely as a result of Henry's help to the explorers.

Henry's warm interest in peoples led him beyond the investigation of topography, geological formations, rocks, and fossils only. Research into the history of America's oldest inhabitants was begun as a result of such expeditions. The rich collections brought back by scientists who accompanied the explorers told of Indian art, languages, tribal life, medical practices, myths, religions, and songs.

"Whatever relates to the nature of man is interesting to the students of every branch of knowledge; and hence ethnology affords a common ground on which the cultivators of physical science, of natural history, of archeology, of language, of history, and of literature, can all harmoniously labor," he wrote in the Smithsonian Report of 1860.

The collection of specimens, relics, and monuments of the prehistoric age were for him not "mere curiosities . . . to excite the wonder of the illiterate," but vivid materials from which to reconstruct the history of the past and relate it to the present. When in 1879 Congress created the Bureau of American Ethnology, the Smithsonian handed over to the new organization more than 670 Indian vocabularies and many other items pertaining to the Indian civilization. According to Dr. Leonard Carmichael, the present Secretary, "The Institution is the authority on virtually every scientific aspect of Indian life."

With Henry's help a great national herbarium—a collection of plants gathered by the exploring expeditions—was established. This rich store of plant life was classified and mounted in the Smithsonian, by Henry, working closely with his old friends John Torrey, botanist, and Asa Gray, naturalist. Later some 30,000 botanical specimens were transferred to the Department of Agriculture, while a mass of bones and other anatomical specimens went to the Army Medical Museum.

Throughout the early years of his own investigations, Henry had smarted under the difficulties of obtaining up-to-the-minute information about contributions by other scientists. And his own work had been virtually buried in two American journals. How accessible were these to European scientists, or for that matter, to young American workers searching in woefully incomplete libraries? The idea came to him to prepare an index of scientific writings. In a report, he voiced the need for one of the basic tools of an investigator—a classified breakdown of previously reported work.

"One of the most important means of facilitating the use of libraries is well-digested indexes of subjects, not merely referring to volumes or books, but to memoirs, papers, and parts of scientific transactions." Everyone who, like himself, was in the business of "enlarging the bounds of human knowledge," should know what had been done in the same line. This he could accomplish by means of careful and complete indexes, Henry insisted.

Unfortunately he was hampered by lack of funds for trained bibliographers; so, in order to carry out this idea he turned to the British Association for cooperation. When the first volume of *Catalogue of Scientific Papers* appeared in 1863, twelve years after Henry had thought of it, the editors gave credit to Henry as the originator of bibliographic indexing:

"The present undertaking may be said to have originated in a communication from Dr. Joseph Henry, Secretary of the Smithsonian Institution," the editors acknowledged.

Carrying out what he thought was Smithson's purpose in his legacy, Henry encouraged original investigations in the Smithsonian laboratories as well as in the far-flung fields where expeditions were digging for knowledge; he helped to train scientific workers, fostered and strengthened scientific societies, saw to the publication of technical papers and specialists' handbooks, and promoted the widest exchange of scientific information throughout the reading world.

Always conscious of the need to keep the capital of the Smithson fund intact, he succeeded in preserving the original bequest, thus assuring the continuation of its glorious work. After Henry's death, the fund itself amounted to $686,000, while the value of the library, the stock of publication, laboratory equipment, and the Smithsonian building amounted to $782,000. Through careful management—guarding against duplication, releasing fledgling activities that could fend for themselves, nurturing new organizations and activities—he guided the Institution along the principles on which it operates to this day: "The great object is to facilitate in every way the promotion of science, and especially the fostering of original research, and enlarging the bounds of human thought."

When the cemetery in Genoa, Italy, where Smithson was buried, fell into neglect, Congress voted to bring the remains of the great benefactor to Washington. Alexander Graham Bell, one of the regents of the Institution, was chosen to go to Italy on this mission of homage. In 1904 James Smithson's remains were given burial with full military honors in a small chapel in the Institution.

If the spirit of James Smithson hovers over his last mortal home, it must look down with great content upon the work he made possible. Under the frustration and emotions of revenge that prompted his bequest to America was the soul of a true scientist. Joseph Henry, "enlarging the bounds of human thought," accomplished all that the donor had vaguely expressed, and much more. Because he was great and untrammeled, Henry enlarged the bounds of his assignment to meet the needs of future generations and to extend the vast, ever-growing wealth of human knowledge.

CHAPTER 12

Obstacles Overcome

HENRY had fully expected, when he took on the job of seeing a public institute through its growing pains, that there would be troubles as well as the joys of achievement. In a letter to Mr. Nott of Union College in December 1846 he had this to say about his intentions: "My object at present is to prevent the adoption of plans which may tend to embarrass the future usefulness of the Institution. . . . The income of the Institution is not sufficient to carry out a fourth of the plans mentioned in the Act of Congress, and contemplated in the reports of the Regents. . . . I have elaborated a simple plan of organization which I intend to press with all my energy. If this is adopted I am confident the name of Smithson will become familiar to every part of the civilized world."

This he lived to see, but there were many battles along the way. Anticipating obstacles, he told Mr. Nott that if he did not succeed in carrying through his plans he would withdraw from the Institution. In the skirmish over the construction of the Smithsonian building Henry suffered defeat. He would have been happy with a simple structure housing his office staff, the laboratory, and necessary library facilities, but on this point he was forced to yield to the desires of Congress, the Board of Regents, and others who clamored for a showy monument. He had thought it wise to give in on this issue for the sake of larger gains he hoped to achieve for the advancement of science. When attractive offers came his way that would have taken him out of the inevitable battles, he declined, because he was "in honor committed to the Institution."

The next battle he fought through to victory. The proponents of a great national library were adamant: Why should not the Smithsonian vie with the British Museum and the Bibliothèque in Paris? The library faction on the Board included the learned Senator Rufus Choate, himself a great book collector, and Charles C. Jewett, the Smithsonian librarian. They stubbornly pursued the idea of a vast library, Choate insisting on the purchase of $20,000 worth of books each year.

"But such an expenditure would cripple other activities of the Institution," we can imagine Henry protesting. "Besides, think of what it will cost to catalogue, bind, and maintain such a collection!"

Jewett, distinguished for his work in preparing the cataloguing rules now used universally in libraries, was ambitious for his department. He demanded an expenditure for books that would have wrecked the remaining operations of the Institution. He threatened to create trouble if he didn't get his way. Following through on his threat, he took the matter to the Board of Regents, over Henry's head, criticizing the Secretary's management of his duties.

Henry was faced with the choice of tolerating this act of insubordination or of losing a most able librarian. To preserve his authority as executive head, he chose to dismiss Jewett. Jewett fought back, publicly challenging Henry's right to dismiss him. The Regents appointed a committee to look into the matter; after an investigation the Board decided that Henry was within his rights.

The affair caused Choate to resign from the Board of Regents in anger, and as a result, the Board itself came under fire. A Congressman from Vermont, intent on showing visiting constituents an imposing library, induced Congress to set up an investigating committee. The imbroglio aroused editorial comment in the newspapers with Henry and the Institution as the targets.

The Congressional committee vindicated Henry, but this did not end the matter. The fact that a citizen of Choate's prominence was critical of Smithsonian policy reflected not only on the Secretary but on the wisdom of the Board in backing him. There followed much meaningless debate about science versus literature, plus vindictive mud-slinging in the press.

Henry was most unhappy over the uproar. Not only did he lose a staff member whose professional ability he regarded highly, but the incident involved Congress in useless wrangling and brought humiliation to those Board members who had placed their confidence in him.

However, the majority of the Board stood behind him, and the tempest blew itself out. Henry's final vindication came when in 1866 the Smithsonian book collection was transferred to the Library of Congress.

As late as 1852, when one would have thought that Henry's plan was well established, there were still greedy ones who turned toward the slim Smithsonian fund for the financing of some pet projects. This time, Senator Stephen A. Douglas, "the Little Giant of Illinois," and one of the best orators of the Middle West, was angling for the farmer's vote, and

Smithsonian Institution Building (Matthew Brady photograph taken no later than January 1865)

hoped the Smithsonian would serve his political purpose. He headed an Agricultural Convention which was held in the lecture hall of the Smithsonian. One of the proposals was to petition Congress for an Agricultural Bureau, to be financed by the Institution. It was a clever attempt to avoid making the taxpayers pay for what was undoubtedly a popular project. If Douglas could swing this plan, it would further his burning ambition to become the country's President.

Douglas brought forth his best political oratory. His argument, designed to carry the audience, had a certain cogency. Without agriculture, civilized man was nothing but a barbarian, he asserted. Smithson had left his money for the advancement of American civilization. To what better use could this money be put than for the benefit of the farmers who were the very basis of this civilization?

The audience greeted the proposal with hearty applause. Henry, seated at the back of the room, realized this was a crisis. Here was a popular leader offering sympathetic listeners a free project they very much wanted. How could anyone oppose the move?

Professor Henry rose to his feet, quietly introduced himself as the Secretary of the Smithsonian Institution, the rightful keeper of the fund they were after, and addressed himself to the farmers, keeping to Senator Douglas's lofty plane.

Could the farmers really think of putting their own needs above those of all men? If they pressed a claim for these funds, weren't they betraying the trust of the generous donor?

Counting on the sound judgment of his listeners, Henry explained the Institution's function to provide and extend the knowledge that would some day be applied to the useful arts. It was by these means that the Institution had already done much to raise the farmers from the level of soil-scratchers to intelligent tillers of the soil, he continued. In the long run they would be the beneficiaries of new truths revealed by the efforts of the Institution. Wouldn't it therefore be short-sighted to rob the organization of the means of improving their lives? His persuasive manner and deep sincerity stirred the audience.

The proponents of the scheme were stunned. And Henry, quick to sense that he had won his point, quietly sat down. Douglas came away from the meeting with a healthy respect for the professor. The two men shook hands afterward and the proposal for an Agricultural Bureau supported by Smithsonian funds was dropped. Two years later Douglas was elected to the Board of Regents. He served for seven years and learned to appreciate the purpose of the Institution, and the integrity and capability of the man who steered its policies.

Henry's devotion to the Institution which had become his life frequently brought him into other such conflicts with men who coveted the funds for their own interests or who tried to perpetuate the encumbrances Congress had originally included in the Act. With patience and tact he aimed first to win the Board of Regents to his policy; gradually he freed the Institution of activities which he thought were not properly in its domain. Distasteful and distracting as these conflicts were, they were but ripples in the otherwise smooth current of his life at the Smithsonian.

But then a more personal storm broke. The man who had refused to protect his discoveries by patents was suddenly drawn into a bitter battle with the patentees of the telegraph. The story takes us back to 1837.

It will be remembered that Samuel Morse was fortunate enough to have met Professor Gale, who had shown him that his defective telegraph required Henry's intensity magnet and battery of many plates. After use of these, Morse's crudely constructed instrument promised to be practicable. But his troubles were far from over.

In September of 1837, Morse invited a group of professors and friends to see his telegraph in operation in Gale's lecture room at the University. By chance, a young man from Morristown, New Jersey, who had dropped out of his theology classes, and given up his plan to become a minister, was visiting the University. As he was walking down the corridor past Gale's room, the door opened and the professor called to him. "Go in there, Vail; you will see something you never saw in my class."

The young man was Alfred Vail, son of Judge Stephen Vail, proprietor of the prosperous Speedwell Iron and Brass Works. Vail had spent many leisure hours in his father's foundry, where the propeller shaft of the *Savannah,* the first steamship to cross the Atlantic, had been forged, and where cylinders for locomotives were at that moment being cast. The young man was handier with tools and metals than with books, and his inventive skill was just what Morse could use to develop the telegraph instruments for successful operation.

Before the month was out, Morse and Vail entered into an agreement, just after Morse had filed the description of his

Samuel F. B. Morse, near the age of 41, at about the time he was working on his telegraph

invention with the United States Patent Office. By this agreement Vail became Morse's partner in the development of the telegraph. Vail was to construct, at his own expense, the instruments needed to demonstrate the operation of the telegraph before a Congressional committee the following January. For his continued services and the work to be done at the Vail shop, Morse agreed to pay him a fourth interest in the invention in the United States and a half interest in Europe, should Vail at his own expense obtain patents in foreign countries.

By this agreement Morse obtained not only the skill of a master metal worker to turn his home-made device into a finished recording mechanism, but also the money and materials to develop the invention. Vail's confidence in its success was so great that he induced his wealthy father and brother to finance Morse in securing the patent. The lever that made dots and dashes was Vail's construction, but the contract called for every improvement to be credited as a Morse invention.

From then on inventor and partner worked for nearly seven more years before the famous message, "WHAT HATH GOD WROUGHT," wired by Morse from Washington, was received by Vail in Baltimore.

During this time Henry at Princeton had given Morse not only heartening encouragement but much-needed technical advice. Neither Morse nor Vail had enough basic knowledge of electricity to carry their project to completion. When the cable was being laid, a new and unexpected problem in insulation threatened to wreck the whole scheme. They had laid the line in lead pipe, but the insulation was faulty, and it had to be torn up. Vail now proposed that they attach the wires on overhead poles, and Morse took a trip to New York to get the necessary fixtures.

Alfred Vail

On his way he stopped at Princeton to visit with his friend and adviser. When Henry inquired about his progress with the telegraph, Morse explained how they had planned to place the wires on poles in the air.

"How do you propose to insulate the wires at the attachment to the poles?" Henry asked.

When Morse explained Vail's plan, Henry immediately declared: "It will not do; you will meet the same difficulty you had in the pipes."

Then Henry, the teacher, explained the physics of running a bare wire overhead, a *single wire* with the ends sunk in wells.

"Clearly, your idea of suspending wires from posts is dangerous," he continued. "The wires would surely be blown against each other by the wind."

"But then, Professor, how do you make the circuit?" Morse was puzzled.

"Bury your wire; use the earth to carry the fluid for you," Henry told the astonished inventor.

"But when did you find this out, Mr. Henry?"

"In running my wire through the air over to Philosophical Hall, I used the ground circuit after Karl Steinheil had discovered it in Germany. The idea isn't patented, and you can use it too."

At this point Professor Henry explained that great discoveries belong to everyone who can use them. The inventor must borrow them from whoever discovered them.

Morse left Professor Henry's laboratory ready to complete the last step in his great invention. That he later forgot his indebtedness to Henry was an affront that the magnanimous Henry took in his stride. And when in 1845 Vail published a history of the electromagnetic telegraph in America, with no mention of Henry's contribution then or in a second printing two years later, Henry kept his feelings to himself.

After two years of backbreaking labors and harsh disappointments, Morse had his final trimph. But he had become rabidly resentful of any suggestion that the success of his invention rested on the work of a long line of pioneers—Franklin, Sturgeon, Steinheil, his engineers Vail and Cornell, and Joseph Henry.

On one occasion when Professor Sears Walker was preparing a report for the Coast Survey on the value of the telegraph system, he called a conference which included Morse, Gale, and Henry. Morse made the astounding statement that he had not known of Henry's discovery at Albany, and had to be reminded by Gale that he had told him in 1837 of the professor's work. When the Walker report was completed, Morse, at Walker's request, sent him a note to append to the report, in which he made the grandiose gesture of seeming to "do justice to Professor Henry."

"While, therefore, I claim to be the first to propose the use of the electro-magnet for telegraph purposes, and the first to construct a telegraph on the basis of the electro-magnet, yet to Professor Henry is unquestionably due the honor of the discovery of a fact in science which proves the practicability of exciting magnetism through a long coil. . . ."

Since Morse left it to Walker's discretion to append the note, the latter, knowing the full facts, thought it wiser to omit a statement which did more for the acknowledger than the acknowledged.

It was inevitable that with the successful operation of the telegraph, many competitors would try to enter the field. Some were only imitators, but others came forward with improvements. These, like Morse before them, had the right to build on established physical laws, to use the knowledge that becomes the heritage of all the people. It was Morse's fate as the owner of the patent to become entangled in litigation with those who rightly or wrongly challenged the legal rights of the Magnetic Telegraph Company (Morse's concern) to construct a line from New York to Washington.

The first of a series of Morse suits for infringements on his patent was against one Henry O'Rielly, who had built a line to the West, under license from the company and had then attempted to establish a branch line without such authority. And it was the ironical fate of Henry, who had rejected any monetary benefits from his discoveries, to become a principal in a bitter controversy over the spoils.

Henry had no interest in the battle between Morse and his rivals. But he was subpoenaed to appear on the witness stand in the case of *Morse vs. O'Rielly,* in Boston, in September 1847. He was asked to answer a number of written questions, and his testimony was a simple recital of the facts:

The instrument that made use of combined circuits and to which Morse held the patent was known both to himself and Sir Charles Wheatstone before 1837.

The battery used by Morse was not his own invention.

Steinheil was the first to use ground circuits and the glass insulators for attaching the wire to the pole. This means of insulation Henry had explained to Morse, making possible the successful operation of the first line.

Without taking undue credit to himself, Henry was generous in his praise of Morse's contribution. Repeating the substance of what he had written to Morse in 1842, he said: "I thought his plan was better than any with which I had been made acquainted in Europe; I became interested in him and instead of interfering with his application to Congress,. I subsequently gave him a certificate in the form of a letter, stating my confidence in the practicability of the electromagnetic telegraph, and my belief that the form proposed by himself was the best that had been published."

But Morse, obsessed by the idea that he and he alone was the inventor of the telegraph, was not satisfied with the court's decision in his favor in the O'Rielly case. He felt that his vindication could come only by stripping Henry of all credit. During the trial even Leonard Gale, who had been neutral in the squabble, was somehow confused enough by Morse's lawyers to testify that when he first saw Morse's telegraph it worked—an error he later corrected.

To Henry, the innocent bystander, the events surrounding

the ten-year telegraph quarrel were most distressing. The lawsuits continued, and the dailies in New York, Philadelphia, Chicago, and Europe, as well as the penny papers in every small town, had a field day. In England, where Wheatstone was the telegraph hero, sentiment was in favor of Henry, as the victim of a man who had profited by his ideas. In the United States too, the aggressiveness of the patentees didn't help their reputation. The press, gathering its news partly from O'Rielly's telegraph, was influenced by the continued refusal of the Morse group to compromise. People were sure that the nullification of the O'Rielly contract by the patentees came from a desire to garner a larger share of the stock on the Western line than had been originally agreed upon.

Morse's fears of losing his telegraph empire were deepened by the imminent expiration of his patent, and he wanted to make certain that he would secure extension. The Patent Commissioner had to consider the possibility that its extension might suppress improvements from other sources. Had Henry wished to do so he could have used his influence to clip Morse's wings. But when he was consulted, he generously recommended that Morse's patent be extended.

When Morse had been granted the extension, he renewed his attack upon the man who, more than anyone else, had supported his claim. In this, Morse enlisted the help of a journalist, Taliafero P. Schaffner, who hoped to capitalize on the dispute to increase the circulation of his short-lived publication, the *Telegraph Companion*. Schaffner devoted an entire issue to Morse's "Defense against the injurious deductions drawn from the deposition of Professor Henry."

In this "defense" Morse flatly stated: "I shall show that I am not indebted to him [Henry] for any discovery in science bearing upon the telegraph; and that all the discoveries of principles having this bearing, were made, not by Professor Henry, but by others, and prior to any experiments of Professor Henry in the science of electro-magnetism."

Much as the sensitive scientist smarted under this latest effrontery, he would have, as a private citizen, hesitated to reply. But in his position he could not ignore what amounted to libel. As Secretary of the Smithsonian Institution, he felt that this was an attack against him as a public figure, and that the honor of the Smithsonian itself was at stake. He therefore refrained from rushing into print with a personal defense. Instead he brought the matter to the Board of Regents, requesting them to appoint a committee to investigate his claims to the original work in telegraphy.

With cool objectivity he once more recited the facts about his work. Further, he called on all those who could competently testify in his behalf. Thus, Samuel F. Chase, the attorney in some of the suits, testified that Henry had at no time tried to take undue credit to himself, "or to detract from the due claims of Morse." The Commissioner of Patents recalled Henry's recommendation that Morse's patent be extended. Gale told how he had acquainted Morse with Henry's contribution in the early days when Morse definitely needed help. Finally, James Hall, geologist for New York State, gave his eyewitness testimony. He told how Amos Eaton had invited him to visit the Albany Academy in 1832, where he saw the little bell and the mile of wire connected with the battery—Henry's audible circuit, the marvel he had seen with his own eyes.

The Regents' committee completely exonerated Henry from the charges in Morse's article: "The first thing which strikes the reader of the article is that its title is a misnomer. It is simply an assault upon Professor Henry, an attempt to disparage his character; to deprive him of his honors as a scientific discoverer; to impeach his credibility as a witness and his integrity as a man . . . Mr. Morse's charges not only remain unproved but they are positively disproved."

So ended the long and painful dispute which made more friends for Henry than for his ambitious opponent, insanely jealous of his claim to fame and fortune.

CHAPTER 13

Family and Friends

FINALLY rid of a quarrel not of his making, the professor returned to his work without a sign of bitterness. That Henry came out of this and other battles unscathed and vigorous was only partly due to his strength of character and deep dedication to his work. Perhaps Rev. Dod's comment on his character helps to explain his freedom from rancor: "Modest, unassuming, gentle in his deportment, he bore the fruit of Christian faith in his life . . . 'When he was reviled, he reviled not again; when he was persecuted, he threatened not.' " Then, too, his happy family life helped him weather the periodic storms that broke over the Smithsonian.

There are only fragments of information available about Henry's home life and his family: his daughter Mary's scattered diary and unsuccessful attempt at a biography of her father, part of Henry's "journal" of the European trip, a few family letters, and the comments of those who visited the Henry home, are the known sources.

About Harriet, his wife, we can only glean that in her self-effacing devotion to Joseph she completely and happily merged her life with his. When he shut the door of his office at the end of the day, he left behind the hurts, bruises, and petty irritations, confident that in his cheerful household he would find solace, sympathetic understanding, and the satisfaction of being king in his own home.

Of the six children who were born to the Henrys, two died in infancy. The others--William, Mary, Helen, and Caroline—even as adults stayed close to home, the girls never having married. They were an affectionate, closely knit family. Especially during the later years of Henry's life, they were deeply involved in their father's scientific and professional affairs.

Mary wrote: "In his family, Father it seemed to us was perfection, tender as a woman, sympathizing with us his children, in all our pleasure and interests even to the smallest particular. We could not but idolize him. He was in a certain way very dependent upon us, requiring attention in many little ways, a kind of helplessness which was a delight to us, as it gave us a vent for our affection. We used to say: 'Father, how do you manage when you are away from home?'—'I always find someone to take care of me,' " he would reply.

Mary tells also about her father's extreme modesty . . . ". . . he was always surprised at the honor paid him," she wrote. "We often said to him, 'You have no idea what a great man you are.' "

Once in Philadelphia he fell ill. The president of a railroad offered to send him home in his private car. "How very kind," Henry remarked. "I do not see why such things are done for me."

He laughed as he recalled how a railway conductor had once told him that he was a remarkable man. Returning from Staten Island he noticed that the car in which he was traveling remained some distance from the depot when it reached Washington. On recognizing his passenger, the conductor said: "Oh Professor Henry, it shall be taken in immediately." At

From left to right: Caroline, Mary, and Helen Henry, Joseph's daughters (probably in early 1860s)

Henry's look of surprise, he added: "This wouldn't be done for an ordinary man."

"Am I not an ordinary man?" the professor asked.

"No, you are an *extraordinary* man," the conductor replied.

At his fireside, the dignified scientist was a kindly and unspoiled human being. His daughters' friends, whom he called "lassies," found him "amusing and genial," and he delighted in their carefree laughter. Little children called him by what they supposed was his first name: "Henry and I are going to do so and so," they would announce.

On evenings when there were no visitors, the family always enjoyed things together, as Mary described in her diary: "Had Father with us all the evening. I modelled his profile in clay while he read Thomson's *Seasons* to us. In the earlier part of the evening he seemed restless, but the influence of the poet drove away the cloud, and then an expression of almost child-like sweetness rested on his lips, singularly in contrast yet beautifully in harmony with the intellect of the brow above."

Turning the pages of the diary at random: "We were all up until a late hour, reading poetry with Father and Mother, Father being the reader. He attempted *Cowper's Grave* by Mrs. Browning, but was too tenderhearted to finish the reading of it. We then laughed over the *Address to the Mummy,* soared to heaven with Shelley's *Skylark,* roamed the forest with Bryant, culled flowers from other poetical fields, and ended with *Tam O'Shanter.* I took for my task to recite a part of the latter from memory, while Father corrected, as if he were 'playing schoolmaster.' "

In this harmonious atmosphere, Henry enjoyed the informal poetry readings or listened to one of his daughters entertaining the family at the piano. In the relaxed moments at home, he displayed his love of the best in literature. He would often quote from memory choice passages—witty, sentimental, moralistic, or humorous—to drive home a point in conversation.

William, the eldest, a source of great pride to his parents and devoted to his sisters, was suddenly taken from them in 1859. A graduate of Princeton, he began his career as a scientist at his father's side in the Institution. His death came just as he was about to leave to begin the study of medicine.

His father's grief is expressed in a letter to James Hall on January 2, 1860. "Sympathy is most grateful to the wounded spirit," he began.

> Sudden and unexpected departure has plunged our family into the deepest sorrow. . . . He was of much assistance to me in the conduct of the affairs of the Institution. . . . His position in the Institution did not well suit his sensitive

> and retiring character, since from the fact that he was my son his acts were observed with a more critical spirit, than would have been had he not been thus related to me. Indeed I failed to do him justice in the way of salary and demands on his time simply because he was, as it were, a part of myself. I had concluded however just before his death to separate him from the Institution and give him an opportunity to complete a course of medical studies, to which he had paid considerable attention; but this resolve came too late. It has pleased the all Wise Disposer of events to take him off in the flower of his age before he had brought forth the fruits of which his talents and acquirements gave promise.
>
> His death has taken my desire to live and were it not that I am anxious as to the future conditions of my family, I would scarcely wish to continue longer to fight the battle of life particularly in the present unhappy conditions of our country and the darkness which rests on the future. . . .

The bereaved father was referring to the gathering clouds of the Civil War.

When the Smithsonian building was finally completed, several years after its official opening in 1847, the Henrys were provided with a seven-room apartment on the second floor of the east wing. The rooms, once the scene of family intimacies, intellectual conversations, and scientific conferences, are now offices, and the Henry dining room the meeting place of the Regents.

Professor Henry's home had another, less intimate side. The Smithsonian apartment was the hospitable center of the intellectual and scientific community in Washington. One room was set aside for guests—distinguished visitors from abroad, or American scientists coming to the capital on professional errands. Often they were accompanied by their wives. The

Studio in the Smithsonian Institution, possibly used by the Henry daughters (photograph probably taken in early 1860s)

Henrys were always glad to entertain such close friends as Dr. and Mrs. James Hall, the Sillimans of Yale, or Louis and Elizabeth Agassiz from Harvard. The Espys and the Baches often dropped in for an evening.

Among his peers Henry had a wide circle of friends—James Dwight Dana, geologist and explorer, John Torrey, botanist, Robert Hare, chemist, Asa Gray, America's foremost botanist—the leading contemporary American scientists. Just as often prominent political figures were guests—Stephen Douglas, John Calhoun, Jefferson Davis, and President Lincoln.

All admired his powerful intellect, keen wisdom, inexhaustible knowledge, and lively interest in people. Asa Gray once wrote: "In the evening we fell to discoursing on philosophical topics, and Henry threw out great and noble thoughts, and as we both fell to conversing with much animation my headache disappeared entirely. There is no man from whom I learn so much as Henry. He calls out your own powers, too, surprisingly."

Far from being shut out from these stimulating evenings, the family shared in entertaining and being entertained by the guests. Often Bache and Douglas would stop by for supper

Library, probably in Joseph Henry apartment in Smithsonian Institution (photograph probably taken in early 1860s)

Bedroom, probably in Henry apartment at Smithsonian (photograph probably taken in early 1860s)

before a meeting, and sometimes the entire Board of Regents would be dinner guests. The discussion at the dinner table was not always on matters of business. Mary recounted stories the brilliant Mrs. Agassiz told of certain drawbacks in living with a naturalist husband. Early in their married life she awoke one night to find a snake coiled in her shoe at the bedside. When her screams aroused Louis Agassiz, he merely asked sleepily: "Oh, where are the rest of them?" He had collected several snakes on an afternoon ramble and brought them home tied in his handkerchief. Of course the creatures had escaped. Professor Agassiz was always absent-minded about such things.

Life in the Henry household was richly satisfying, brimming with warm hospitality, intellectually stimulating and at times exciting, but it was never lavish. Luckily the Henrys had simple tastes, for on the Secretary's salary Mrs. Henry had to manage a modest household. Though she had grown up in a wealthy home, she had long ago learned to live within her husband's smaller means.

Henry's annual salary as Secretary was, at first, $3,500 a year. When an increase was voted for him, he declined it because the members of his staff were not given increases as well. It was only many years later when this was no longer a drawback that he accepted a salary rise. After nearly twenty years at the Institution, his salary was $4,500.

Once pledged to the Smithsonian, he repeatedly turned down more lucrative positions. When Dr. Robert Hare resigned his professorship of chemistry in the medical department of the University of Pennsylvania, the trustees offered Henry the vacant chair. The salary was more than double what he was getting as Secretary, and the position offered the opportunity for research in one of the greatest universities in the country. Yet he readily gave up what must have been a tempting offer rather than abandon his sacred trust.

Similarly he declined invitations to go to Harvard as professor, to South Carolina University as head of a department, and to Princeton as president. Though his domestic finances were often strained by his generous entertaining of scientific and official Washington, he gave up such customary additions to a professor's income as fees from lectures or the publication of books. Personal ambition for wealth or fame was foreign to his nature.

His attitude toward personal wealth was expressed in a letter to his friend Robert Patterson: "I resolved at an early age to preserve my independence by never expending more than my income, and since I have been in public life I have studiously avoided accepting propositions which have been made to me to lend my name to the advocacy of any enterprises of a speculative nature, or to accept the offered means which have been presented to me, for acquiring property, but which might compromise my independence in regard to public acts."

CHAPTER 14

For Science and Country

MUCH OF Henry's time was taken up with administrative duties at the Institution, many of them humdrum, but scientific investigation also had its place in the busy years. Perhaps he would have preferred to work on some abstract principle, but he showed no snobbery toward any project that promised to be of immediate practical benefit to the government or to the general public.

In the early 1850s President Fillmore turned to him with an inquiry about the strength of building materials. The Capitol was being extended, and Henry was one of a committee to study the long-term durability of building stones. His fertile mind was immediately challenged. "While the exterior materials of a building are to be exposed for centuries," he said, "the conclusions to be desired are to be drawn from results produced in the course of a few weeks. Besides this, in the present state of science, we do not know all the actions to which all the materials are to be subjected by nature, nor can we fully estimate the amount of those which are known."

He went to work. Samples of marble cut into cubes were put into a steel press to test their resistance to crushing. The procedure was then repeated with a sheet of lead above and below the block, to test the practice then in use of placing lead between the stones. He discovered that the bare blocks withstood twice the pressure of the ones with the lead plates. He explained this striking fact by showing that the bare stone gave way by bulging out in the center of each of the four perpendicular sides of the cube, so that all parts of the block broke down together. But when the lead was interposed, the stone gave way first along the edges at the points of least resistance; the remaining pressure then had to be sustained by the portions around the center of the cube, making it weaker under pressure.

As a result of this interesting finding, lead and all other substances similarly used were discarded. And after devising a way to grind the upper and lower surfaces of the cube "into perfect parallelism," the crushing force that they sustained "was therefore much greater than that heretofore given for the same material," Henry reported.

Acoustics had always been a favorite subject of Henry's. In 1851, he read a paper before the American Association for the Advancement of Science "On the Limit of Perceptibility of a direct and reflected Sound." In it he reported that an echo can be clearly distinguished from the sound itself, if it is reflected from a wall 35 feet away from the sound or the listener. At shorter distances, the echo and sound blended so as not to be distinguishable from each other.

The modern acoustical engineer has many instruments to aid him, but Joseph Henry had only tuning forks, hand-clapping, or his own voice available for carrying out his experiments. His conclusions, confirmed years later with refined instruments, were that the perception of echoes depended partly on pitch (the frequency of air vibrations of length of sound waves) and partly on the sharpness or clearness of the sound. He found that a sound impression on the ear lasted one-sixteenth of a second, which meant that the lowest perceptible musical tone was produced by 16 vibrations per second. He applied these facts to the acoustical requirements of lecture rooms. The ceiling, he said, should be no more than 30 feet high; and if the ceiling is smooth it will tend to reinforce the sound of the speaker's voice.

Using tuning forks, he studied sound conduction by different materials. A tuning fork suspended by a fine thread continues to vibrate for more than four minutes without being heard, but if it is placed on a pine table the same vibration will produce a loud, full tone after only ten seconds. On a marble table top, the sound is much more feeble. The same tuning fork placed against a brick wall gives a feeble tone for 88 seconds; against a lath-and-plaster partition, its sound is louder but continues for only 18 seconds.

On a large block of soft india-rubber resting on a marble slab, the vibration was quickly extinguished, without giving an audible sound. What happened to the sound? To this also Henry found the answer. He inserted a copper and an iron wire into a piece of rubber and connected the ends of the two metals to a thermocouple, and found that the vibrations were converted into heat. From this he concluded that sheets of rubber were among the best absorbers and destroyers of sound.

Some time later, with Alexander Bache, Henry was examining the acoustics of the Smithsonian lecture hall, when President Franklin Pierce invited him to extend his studies to the plans which had been prepared for additional rooms in the Capitol. Henry and the architect set out on a tour of large halls and churches in Philadelphia, New York, and Boston, inspect-

Second floor hallway in east end of old Smithsonian Building. Door at extreme left leads to present Secretary's office

ing and testing their acoustics. Henry checked these observations with experimental tests, and his conclusions concerning the spread and dying out of sound, its absorption and reflection as echoes were reported before the American Association for the Advancement of Science. In 1856, his paper, "On the Acoustics applied to Public Buildings" was published in its proceedings.

In matters of science Henry always showed scrupulous objectivity. One example was his attitude toward the doctrine of evolution which produced a major controversy in his day. The storm which the publication of Darwin's *Origin of Species* aroused in 1859 reached American shores the next year when the book was published in the United States. Scientists promptly went to battle, one camp led by Asa Gray who had enjoyed Darwin's confidence for years before the publication of the theory, and the other by Louis Agassiz who vehemently opposed this view of the development of living things.

Both men were Henry's close friends, but in making up his mind about a fundamental matter of science, Henry ignored his personal attachments and examined the evidence. Despite Agassiz' efforts to convert Henry to the side of the anti-evolutionists, he succeeded only in postponing Henry's verdict. When Henry had examined the facts on a subject not in his own field, he wrote in a detached way to Gray: "I have given the subject of evolution much thought, and have come to the conclusion that it is the best working hypothesis which you naturalists have ever had."

While this expression set him against his cherished friends Agassiz, Torrey, and Guyot, he would not retreat from his position. He was much more outspoken about spiritualists.

In the 1860s, the spiritualist craze was sweeping Washington. Even the family in the White House was going in for table-rapping at seances. There may have been some excuse for poor Mrs. Lincoln who, in her grief over the recent loss of her son, was easily taken in by one of the more persuasive mediums. Henry would have nothing to do with Colchester, the most noted of the impostors who preyed upon credulous folk. But he could not refuse a request of the President's family to arrange a meeting at which Colchester was to demonstrate his "spiritual powers."

The meeting took place at Henry's office in the Smithsonian. Perhaps the medium did not fully appreciate his disadvantage when he tried to convince America's leading acoustics expert that various sounds he created came from different parts of the room. Henry listened patiently, turning his head in the direction from which each sound was supposed to come. When he had satisfied himself of their location, he ended the seance by telling Colchester: "I do not know how you make these sounds, but this I perceive very clearly—they do not come from the room but from your person."

Some time later, in a railroad coach, Henry fell into conversation with a fellow passenger who recognized him. The man proudly told Henry that he was an instrument maker, and this led immediately into talk about electrical instruments. The young manufacturer said that he was making instruments for spiritualistic mediums to use in performing their tricks. Henry asked for the names of some of his customers and discovered that Colchester was among them. Henry told his chance acquaintance about his meeting with Colchester, and said that while he didn't know just how he produced the sounds, he was sure that they came from something concealed on the medium's person. The instrument maker said he was right, and described the gadget Colchester had used. The instrument was fastened around the medium's arm, and gave off clicking sounds when the trickster, without visible movement of his arm, contracted and relaxed his biceps muscle.

At the request of an acquaintance, Henry once attended a seance incognito, and reported that he had seen nothing of a "supernatural character" from this much-lauded medium. To another of his friends who swore that he had himself seen a medium sail through a window, he angrily asserted: "Judge,

Matthew Brady photograph of Joseph Henry, probably taken in late 1860s

you never saw that, and if you think you did, you are in a serious condition and need the utmost care of your family and physician."

The skeptical scientist soon earned such a bad name with spiritualists that they refused to let him test their "supernatural powers."

For nearly a quarter of a century, Professor Henry gave distinguished service to the Light-House Board. Established by act of Congress in 1852, this Board was responsible for the lighthouses along the American coasts. Henry was appointed a board member, and his duties included experiments relating to lights and signals. With the same zeal with which he attacked a problem in electromagnetism, he approached the job of making coastal navigation safe.

His first recommendation was to replace the old heavy and inefficient reflecting mirrors with a modern Fresnel type lens he had seen on his visit to France. The lenses bent the light into parallel bundles that could be beamed in any desired direction. Henry's energy and tact overcame the prejudice against establishment of a new system.

In less than ten years the Fresnel lenses were introduced into all the lighthouses in the United States. And after another decade the 10,000 miles of shore, extending from the St. Croix River in Maine to the mouth of the Rio Grande in the Gulf of Mexico, around the Great Lakes and along the Pacific coast, were illuminated by lighthouse rays, "a mariner rarely losing sight of one light until he has gained another," according to a report of the Light-House Board in 1873.

In the meantime, about 1853, the nation was faced with a problem that called for more than administrative efficiency and sound practical judgment. The lighthouse lamps burned whale oil, but its growing scarcity so increased the cost that a cheaper substitute had to be found. In Europe they were using rapeseed oil, but American farmers could not be induced to cultivate this plant in the necessary quantities. Then lard was suggested as a substitute for sperm oil, but a Baltimore professor's tests showed it to be an inferior illuminant. It was at this point that Henry tackled the problem.

For a dozen or more years he spent part of his vacations at the Light-House Depot on Staten Island. There he constructed a fireproof chamber, painted pitch black inside so that he could conduct accurate light-measuring tests. He tried various illuminants: rapeseed oil, kerosene (newly discovered), and lard. In ordinary lamps, rapeseed oil illuminated as well as whale oil, but lard was inferior, Henry also found; and kerosene proved too dangerous. But he was not one to give up; he went back to study lard.

Experiment showed that lard oil was heavier than sperm oil,

flowed less easily and therefore ascended too slowly through the wick. He then tried burning it at higher temperatures and found that under these conditions lard oil flowed more easily and moved up the wick more rapidly. At 250 degrees Fahrenheit it burned more brightly than whale oil!

When the two oils were compared in the lanterns used in lighthouses, at the greater heat provided by the large Argand burners, lard oil came out ahead in brilliance. Under the conditions in which it was to be used in lighthouses, it was actually better than the early laboratory tests with ordinary lamps had shown. The previously condemned illuminant now proved to be just what was wanted, at one-fourth the cost of whale oil.

Against the opposition of the sperm oil dealers, lard was introduced in 1865, and by the next year it was used in all lighthouses in the United States. Saving a dollar on every gallon, the government spent 100,000 dollars less every year for illuminating oil in lighthouses.

Next Henry turned to a major hazard at sea—fog, the most dreaded of the impediments to navigation. This is work he must have especially enjoyed because it gave him a chance to again work with acoustics. Every kind of noisemaker had been used—bells whistles, gongs, guns, and horns—to give timely warning of impending danger. Gun signals were among the first to be abandoned because they were dangerous, expensive, and inefficient: the long gap between explosions and the shortness of their duration made it difficult for navigators to detect the direction of the sound accurately.

Patent seekers and men bitten by the "invention bug" came with their rattles, horns, trumpets, and organ-pipes to the Light-House Board. Henry lent a patient ear to all of them, trying each device in turn, experimenting with each new size and shape of contraption. "Every theory, plan, or machine, which was pressed on the Board, . . . for the interests of commerce and navigation. . . . [was] examined by its Chairman [of the committee] and . . . formally reported upon. If it had no practical value, the report . . . simply stated the inexpediency of its adoption: but the Professor often verbally pointed out to the presenter its fallacy; and sent him away—if not satisfied—at least feeling that he had been well treated." In these words the Naval Secretary of the Light-House Board reported Henry's services.

In 1867, testing stations were set up at Sandy Hook on the Jersey shore, at the entrance of Raritan Bay and New York Bay. Three sounding devices were systematically tested: a large steam-whistle that could be adjusted for pitch; a reed trumpet 17 feet long, with a flaring mouth 3 feet wide; a siren horn operated by steam at different pressures.

To test the efficiency of each Henry devised a phonometer or "artificial ear"—a membrane stretched across an iron horn and sprinkled with sand. Trumpets curved and straight, square and round, made of wood, brass, and iron; whistles screeching at different pitches and under different pressures of steam were all tested. The fine sand strewn on the membrane was agitated as the membrane vibrated with the sound waves it received from the different noise makers. This was a way of "seeing" sound waves; one didn't have to depend upon the hearer's judgment.

Working on these experiments for several years, in calm weather and under winds of high velocity, on decks of vessels or at the mastheads, in snow, rain, and fog, making exploratory voyages to test his sounding devices, Henry finally concluded that the siren was the most powerful and penetrating of the instruments. Under a pressure of 60 to 80 pounds, and at a pitch between 350 and 400 vibrations per second (about the key of G, above middle C) the best results were obtained. The siren he finally chose was heard at a greater distance during a dense fog than during clear weather—15 to 20 miles away.

In 1871, Henry became Chairman of the Light-House Board. Giving his services free, he attended weekly meetings, inspected lighthouses, set standards, inspired others to apply his wide knowledge of physical principles. "The character of the aids which any nation furnishes the mariner in approaching and leaving its shores, marks in a conspicuous degree its advancement in civilization," he declared in his report in 1874.

CHAPTER 15

Science in War

HENRY, the scientist, always ready to follow the path of investigation as far as it would lead, gave little thought to the less predictable course of history. On the issues of the Civil War the professor lacked the clarity of vision he was able to bring to knotty scientific problems in or out of the laboratory. Probably he considered this tragic struggle outside his domain, though the Smithsonian grounds were within earshot of cannon bursts —a constant grim reminder of the conflict that was tearing the country apart. To Henry it was a shattering, useless strife; he had no hope that it would result in the rebirth of a nation.

In his position, he necessarily associated with leaders of both North and South. Jefferson Davis was a personal friend. Henry did not have a clear understanding of the differing economic and social interests that motivated the North to preserve the Union, and the South to organize a government based on states' rights. This may account for the fact that his attitude toward the conflict was at first colored by the views of the Southern leaders, who were his friends.

He wrote to Asa Gray in 1860 on the question of slavery. He believed, like some contemporaries, that if the status quo were allowed to remain undisturbed, "the whole matter will in due time be settled by the law of population and the conflict of races. Labor from the North, as it is hampered by the increase of laborers must be gradually extended into the South until it is stopped by the heat of the sun. "There are parts of our country which cannot be worked by the white man, and this must be cultivated by the Negro or not at all."

Whatever his private views, as the executive officer of the Institution he felt it his duty to remain neutral on political questions. This naive if honest desire to steer clear of partisanship proved embarrassing on one occasion, when Horace Greeley and Henry Ward Beecher, the abolitionists, were to speak against slavery.

Henry had made it a rule that whenever the Smithsonian lecture hall was used for a meeting, the chairman was to open the meeting with this statement: "I am requested by Professor Henry to announce that the Smithsonian Institution is not in any way responsible for this course of lectures."

After reading the required statement, the chairman continued: "I do so with pleasure and desire to add that the Washington Lecture Association is in no way responsible for the Smithsonian Institution." The remark called forth the expected laughter from the audience, which included Lincoln and some members of his Cabinet. Privately, Lincoln later told Henry, "The laugh was rather on you, Henry." To avoid further jokes of this kind at his expense, Henry thereafter closed the lecture hall to any but scientific meetings.

Henry's staunch espousal of the Union cause came only after he got to know President Lincoln. Mary records in her diary that her father saw Lincoln for the first time officially on May 3, 1861, when he went to the White House to inform Lincoln that, as President of the United States, he was head of the Smithsonian Institution, and was expected to meet with the Regents and the Secretary on the first Tuesday in May.

As they became better acquainted, Henry's admiration for Lincoln grew and flowered into a warm friendship and unswerving loyalty. In 1862, he commented to a Cabinet member: "I have lately met him five or six times. He is producing a powerful impression upon me. It increases with every interview."

In their many encounters in connection with Light-House Board matters and vessels navigating in waters made dangerous by the Confederates, Henry was deeply impressed with the wisdom, knowledge, and purpose of the President. Speaking to a government official one day he said:

> President Lincoln impresses me as a man whose honesty of purpose is transparent, who has no mental reservations, who may be said to wear his heart on his sleeve. He has been called coarse. In my interviews with him he conversed with apparent freedom, and without a trace of coarseness. He has been called ignorant. He has shown a comprehensive grasp of every subject on which he has conversed with me. His views of the present situation are somewhat novel, but seem to me unanswerable. He has read many books and remembers their contents better than I do. . . . I desired him to understand and look favorably upon a change which I wished to make in the policy of the Light-House Board in a matter requiring some scientific knowledge. He professed his ignorance, or rather he ridiculed his knowledge of it, and yet he discussed it intelligently.

In turn, Lincoln confessed that at first: "I had the impression the Smithsonian was printing a great amount of useless information." Later he admitted that "Professor Henry has convinced me of my error. It must be a grand school if it produces such thinkers as he is. He is one of the pleasantest men

I have ever met; so unassuming, simple and sincere. I wish we had a few thousand more such men."

The bitter war years brought the two men even closer. Many a time the President came to seek moments of quiet at the Henry apartment, and to get scientific advice from his dear friend. Occasionally he would stop to watch the scientist at his experiments and help with the apparatus used to test some lighting device.

There were some who continued to suspect Henry of Southern sympathies during the war. This is indicated by the following story: Quite often the people of Washington saw mysterious lights flashing at night from the Smithsonian tower. One day an agitated patriot came to see the President on urgent business of national importance. When admitted, the stranger saw the President had a visitor whom he did not recognize as Professor Henry. When the man hesitated to tell his story in the presence of another, Lincoln assured him the gentleman enjoyed his confidence.

The caller then told Lincoln that the lights he saw nightly must be signals from a traitor at the Smithsonian, directed to the Rebels across the Potomac. Lincoln burst into laughter, explaining that the flashing lights were tests of the Army's new blinker signals, and that he himself often accompanied Professor Henry to the tower for these experiments.

During the war, Henry's help was sought, not only by President Lincoln, but also by the War, Navy, and Treasury Departments, whose executives were besieged by people advancing every imaginable kind of scheme for saving the country.

Torpedo balloons, explosives that promised to outdo gunpowder, cheap methods for the manufacture of paper money, ways of preventing counterfeiting—devices for engraving, secret

Last photograph of Joseph Henry

markings, anti-photographing inks, novel textures of paper—were only some of the ingenious schemes that Henry was called upon to evaluate.

In this troublesome and often disagreeable task his recommendations sometimes shattered the hopes of aspirants to fame and fortune. But once he was convinced of the fraudulence or chicanery of an adventurer, his decision was inflexible. On the other hand, his help in separating the worthless from the useful made it possible for the rare proposals of real merit, that might otherwise have been overlooked by hasty officials with no scientific background, to be given proper attention.

Just after the firing on Fort Sumter started the "Brothers' War," Professor Thaddeus S. C. Lowe begged the Union Army to use observation balloons. Everywhere his proposal met with cold indifference. But Henry encouraged Lowe to continue with his tests and introduced him to President Lincoln. Ballooning up from the Smithsonian grounds, Lowe described from an aerial view the scene before him, sending the message by telegraph wire to Lincoln in the White House. Thus, the Smithsonian, the "incubator" of American science, became also the midwife of the U. S. Air Force. With Henry's and Lincoln's support, Lowe became chief of the new Army Balloon Corps. His hydrogen-filled aircraft spied on Confederate armies, directed artillery bombardments, and ferreted out the Rebels' secrets so effectively that General McClellan told the aeronaut: "You are the eyes of the Army."

Another military task that Henry accomplished was the preparation of disinfectants for army hospitals. The miserable sheds hastily set up near the Smithsonian where Walt Whitman and others nursed the wounded—friend and foe alike—ran out of disinfectants. The medical officer in charge turned to Professor Henry for help. The laboratory staff at the Smith-

Photograph probably taken January 24, 1865, at the time of the burning of the Smithsonian Institution, and reproduced in *Harpers Weekly*. Added fire and smoke not entirely accurate as to location

sonian was immediately enlisted to prepare the much-needed chemicals.

In such ways Henry assisted and strengthened the Government during the years of its greatest trial. Actually, the record of Henry's inestimable services as scientific adviser, expert, and arbiter is far from complete. Most of these records were lost in the fire of 1865 that destroyed the interior of the two north towers of the Institution.

Henry took this great loss with resignation, writing to Torrey: "A few years ago, such a calamity would have paralyzed me for future effort, but in my present view of life I take it as the dispensation of a kind and wise providence, and trust that it will work to my spiritual advantage."

CHAPTER 16

The Last Years

IN 1863, during the critical days of the Civil War, the National Academy of Sciences was created as an outgrowth of the permanent Commission to advise the Navy Department. Although Henry was not a charter member, his name was so closely linked with it that he is shown among the founders in the painting in the Academy Building. He actively supported the work of Bache, its first president, and James Dwight Dana, vice-president. In 1865 he wrote its first annual report because Bache was ill, and when Dana resigned Henry was elected to fill his post, and frequently also performed the duties of the ailing president. Bache never regained his health, and on his death in 1867, Henry was elected president, holding office for eleven years.

One of the purposes of the Academy was to give recognition to men who advanced science by original research. Henry had always felt "that men who enlarged the field of human thought" not otherwise rewarded—by wealth, political power, and military honor—should be honored by their government. "The establishment of this Academy may be perhaps regarded as having opened a fourth avenue for the aspirations of a laudable ambition," its new president wrote. His advocacy of the scientist's right to recognition did not spring from personal vanity, for no one had less of this human frailty than Henry.

In 1870, the Regents granted Henry several months' leave for travel abroad. So that he would agree to accept $2,000 for his expenses, they told him he would be making the voyage for the Institution. On June 1st, he sailed with Mary. He revisited the countries he had toured on his earlier trip, and met the new generation of scientists, among them Thomas Huxley and John Tyndall, Faraday's successor. Everywhere he was greeted with praise for his work at the Smithsonian.

He took time out for trips into the countryside, to enjoy the peace and beauty of English landscapes and the scenes immortalized in the poetry he loved so much. The beauties of nature touched him no less than great works of art. Speaking about his sensitivity to all things beautiful, Dr. James C. Welling, President of Columbia University, said Henry "united a heart which was ever ready to leap with joy at the wonder and bloom of the world."

On this trip he visited Switzerland where he had not been before. The magnificent Alpine peaks had special meaning for him because they had so often been described by his Swiss friends, Guyot and Agassiz.

After leaving Aar Glacier where Agassiz had done much of his work in discovering the astonishing fact of the world's Ice Ages, Henry and his daughter crossed over the mountain to the Rhone Valley. A turn in the road revealed the Rhone Glacier in its full majesty. He stood silent and motionless for a few minutes; then, with tears running down his cheeks, he turned to his daughter and said in a stifled voice: "This is a place to die in. We should go no further."

On his return he took part in the organization of the Philosophical Society of Washington (1871) of which he was the leading spirit and president for a number of years. To this day the Society holds an annual Joseph Henry Lecture in his honor.

In the years immediately following, Henry's work at the Smithsonian constantly expanded. His advice and help were sought in the planning stages for the creation of several institutions which were not opened until after his death. The Bureau of Ethnology, established in 1879, was firmly built on the work of Henry; he laid the groundwork also for the creation of the National Museum and the National Zoological Park some years later.

Henry's health was still remarkably good, as it had been most of his life, and he still spent his vacations doing experiments at Staten Island, where he gave his services without pay. He continued this work throughout the summer of 1877.

Toward the end of that year he suffered a temporary paralysis of his right arm, and while he recovered some use of it, he was not well enough to go on with his work.

A thorough physical examination showed that Henry had a serious kidney ailment. When he bluntly asked the doctor how much time he still had, the physican reluctantly admitted that he had only a few months. Henry was about to pay his fee, but the doctor said: "You are not in my debt. There are no debts for the dean of American science."

At a meeting in April 1878 Joseph Henry tendered his resignation as president of the National Academy of Sciences. At this time his friends presented him with a testimonial fund of $40,000 which he accepted on the condition that he and his family would use only the interest. Upon their death the principal would revert to the National Academy of Sciences, the income to be used in perpetuity to assist original research in science.

Tomb of Joseph and Harriet Henry, Oak Hill Cemetery, Washington, D. C.

"I am still impelled to scientific investigation by an instinct, even emotion such as has never deceived me. I still feel the power to dispel darkness to extend light and enlarge the bounds of human thought."

At some time late in life Henry jotted this sentiment down on a scrap of paper. His buoyancy of spirit showed no signs of waning. "... surely no one was ever more successful in retaining life's coveted greenness in age," a fellow scientist said of him.

In his final days when he knew that he might die at any moment, Henry said that he would like to live long enough to complete some of the work he had undertaken, but added to a friend at his bedside: "I have had a happy life, and I hope I have been able to do some good."

One night he talked in his sleep about acoustical experiments. He died the next day, May 13, 1878. He was buried in Oak Hill Cemetery in the Georgetown suburb of the capital. Attending the funeral were President Hayes and members of his Cabinet, justices of the Supreme Court, representatives of foreign governments, and colleagues from the many learned societies in whose work Henry had shared.

In December of that year, the House of Representatives adopted a resolution for a memorial meeting in honor of Joseph Henry, to be held in the Hall of the House of Representatives on January 16, 1879. In this way his government showed its gratitude to a modest man for distinguished service in the advancement of science and for the national good.

In 1880, a bill introduced into the Senate and passed by Congress called for the erection of a bronze statue of Joseph Henry. The statue faces the Administration Building of the Smithsonian Institution, standing guard over the greatest monument that Henry himself created.

A memorial volume was published by the Smithsonian Institution in 1881, containing the commemorative proceedings of various scientific societies and an account of the exercises at the Capitol, during which his friends and fellow scientists expressed their love and esteem for the outstanding scientist of the century.

Moving of Joseph Henry Statue to present location in front of North door of Smithsonian Institution, 1934

Index

Index

Index

Index